Where to Launch around the Coast

Compiled by
Diana van der Klugt

Printed by: ESP, Crowborough, East Sussex

Cover Design: Julia Gray
Cover Photography: Patrick Roach

New edition 1994

ISBN 1 898574 02 2

Copyright © Diana van der Klugt
Opus Book Publishing Limited
Millhouse, Riseden Road, Wadhurst, East Sussex

Whilst every care has been taken in the compilation of this guide, no responsibility can be taken for the existence of any inaccuracies contained in the information published in this book. A reference to any particular site in this book is not evidence of a right of way to the site or of public availability at any time and the inclusion of any slipway in this book cannot be taken as a recommendation of such a site. The publishers do not hold themselves responsible for any accident which arises as a result of any site mentioned in this book being used.

Contents

Introduction

Trail-boats come in many shapes and sizes, from small sailing dinghies to larger powerboats, but they require much the same facility - a good launching site or slipway, to enable them to be put to their proper waterborne use as quickly as possible. They are used by many different types of watersports enthusiasts - waterskiers, dinghy sailors, divers, fishermen, trailer-sailors and especially weekend potterers who live miles from the sea but get enjoyment from visiting different coastal areas. But a good slipway must be able to offer other facilities, in particular parking for car and trailer, and useful amenities such as toilets, fuel or chandlery. All this information and much more, will be found for over 650 sites in WHERE TO LAUNCH AROUND THE COAST.

Using The Book

The book is divided geographically into seven sections, starting with the West Country and then following an anti-clockwise direction around the British Coast: each section is prefaced by a sketch map of the area covered showing the location of the majority of sites and there is also a comprehensive index at the end of the book. Where possible the following details are given for each site:

Name and contact telephone number (where applicable)

Type:	contruction and equipment
Suits:	recommended craft size
Availability:	tidal access or other time constraints
Restrictions:	speed limits, local dangers, prohibition of certain types of craft
Facilities:	availability of fuel, parking for car and trailer, (c) indicates a charge for the facility, toilets, chandlery, diving supplies, outboard repairs etc
Dues:	any harbour or local dues payable
Charge:	launching fee, if applicable; charges quoted are for launching and retrieving a 15' boat unless otherwise stated
Directions:	directions from the nearest main road plus local directions
Waters accessed:	the local bay, estuary, loch or general sea area

Most sites described are suitable for craft up to 18' length over all (LOA) unless specified. A site described as suitable for dinghies only usually has restricted access which may mean that the boat has to be manhandled into the water. The hours of use given for coastal sites are intended as a guide only; obviously this is a matter that depends very much on the type of craft to be launched and on the conditions prevailing at the time. In the case of larger craft, especially those with a deep draught, launching should be undertaken as near high water (HW) as possible although at some exposed sites sea conditions at high water can be dangerous. Many sites can be used to launch smaller craft at most states of tide, especially if the trailer can be manhandled across the beach to the water. Before launching you should always make sure that you are aware of any local restrictions or bye-laws which may be in force. This particularly applies to those wishing to launch powerboats and pwc or to water-ski. In many popular bathing areas, these activities are restricted to clearly defined areas and there are heavy penalties for infringement of the bye-laws; those wishing to water-ski should always be aware of the danger which can be present to bathers. In many harbours, especially those on the South Coast, harbour dues are charged.

Safety
When putting to sea for however long or far, precautions must be taken and certain equipment carried. Remember the following.
1.   Know the limitations of your craft
2.   Learn the "Rules of the Road" and any local bye-laws regarding speed limits, use of craft etc
3.   Seek local knowledge or talk to the coastguard, who can warn of local dangers
4.   Inform someone of where you are going and how long you expect to be away
5.   Listen to local weather forecasts and heed any warnings of adverse weather

All craft should carry:
1.   A means of sound signalling, and navigation lights, if used between sunset and sunrise
2.   An extra means of propulsion, if only oars or paddles
3.   An anchor and plenty of line
4.   A suitable bailer
5.   Lifejackets or buoyancy aids for all the crew, preferably to be worn at all times
6.   Warm and waterproof clothing
7.   Flares: two red hand flares and two orange smoke signals for small craft
8.   Local charts, tide tables and a compass

TRAILERS AND THE LAW

The trailer is very often the neglected part of the boating package. Whilst hulls, engines and other equipment are well maintained the trailer lies idly by, open, unprotected and usually without a squirt of grease. The moment the sun appears, however, it is hitched up with its load and expected to perform perfectly in delivering its charge to the water's edge. Do give it a chance! Protect those bearings with grease and put a dab on the ballhitch. Check the tyres and lights and above all make sure it is legal. Our trailer laws have been brought into line with other EEC countries and you must conform, otherwise you risk your weekend or holiday being marred by a brush with the police.

BRAKING REGULATIONS

Trailers without brakes
You may use an unbraked trailer with a gross weight (total of trailer, boat and contents) of up to 750kg (15cwt), provided the towing vehicle's kerbside weight is at least twice the gross weight of the trailer. All unbraked trailers must be clearly marked with their maximum gross weight and it is an offence to overload the trailer.

Trailers fitted with brakes
The braking system on new trailers must conform with the EEC directive which states that trailers must be fitted with a coupling and correctly matched brakes and linkage which have a minimum braking efficiency of 45% G. They must also be fitted with auto-reverse brakes and have a parking brake capable of holding the trailer stationary on a gradient of 18%. The efficiency of your brakes can be checked at good trailer centres.

2

Trailer dimensions

The maximum width of a trailer when being towed by a motor car or light goods vehicle is 2.3m. In all other cases (HGV) this is 2.5m. The trailer or trailer load must not extend more than 305mm outwards on either side of the towing vehicle. The maximum width allowable, without police advice and supervision, is 2.9m. A trailer and its load must not normally exceed 7m in length excluding drawbar and coupling. Longer loads are permissable for heavy vehicles conforming to certain conditions.

LIGHTING REGULATIONS

Two red tail lights and brake lights must be fitted which operate with the towing vehicle lights. Two amber indicators must flash in unison with the towing vehicle indicators. Two red triangular reflectors of the approved type must be fitted to the rear of the trailer and the number plate area must be illuminated. Trailers exceeding 5m in length must also be fitted with orange side facing reflectors and if the trailer is over 1.6m wide it must also have white front marker lights. The latter are also reqired if the trailer or load project more than 400mm beyond the front position lamps of the towing vehicle. At least one rear fog lamp must be fitted independant of the rear brake lights.

This is only a brief outline of the law affecting trailers and we advise anyone who intends to trail their boat to check on the current regulations in force.

Indespension Ltd publish the "Trailer Manual", a complete guide to trailers and towing. A new edition is expected to be published in summer 1994 and will be obtainable from the company. Contact: Indespension Ltd, Belmont Road, Bolton BL1 7AQ Tel: (0204) 309797

USEFUL ADDRESSES

British Marine Industry Federation (BMIF), Meadlake Place,Thorpe Lea Road,
    Egham, Surrey. Tel: (0784) 472222
British Disabled Water Ski Federation, Heron Lake, Hythe End, Wraysbury,
    Middlesex, TW19 6HW. Tel: (0784) 483664
British Water Ski Federation, 390 City Road, London, EC1V 2QA.
    Tel: (071) 833 2855
Broads Authority, Thomas Harvey House, 18 Colegate, Norwich,
    Norfolk, NR3 1BQ. Tel: (0603) 610734
Dinghy Cruising Association,
    3 Ashley Close, Sevenoaks, Kent, TN13 3AP.
HM Coastguard, Spring Place, 105 Commercial Road, Southampton, Hants, SO15
    1EG. Tel: (0703) 329100
Hydrographic Office, Taunton, Somerset. TA1 2DN, Tel: (0823) 337900
Meteorological Office, London Road, Bracknell, Berks, RG12 2SZ.
    Tel: (0344) 856655
National Federation of Sea Schools, Staddlestones, Fletchwood Lane, Totton,
    Southampton, Hants, SO4 2DZ Tel: (0703) 869956
Royal Institute of Navigation, 1 Kensington Gore, London SW7 2A,
    Tel: (071) 589 5021
Royal Yachting Association, RYA House, Romsey Road, Eastleigh, Hants. SO5 4YA
    Tel: (0703) 629962
Trail Sail Association, Scape Haven, 22 Grand Stand, Scapegoat Hill, Golcar,
    Huddersfield, HD7 4NQ Tel: (0484) 653998

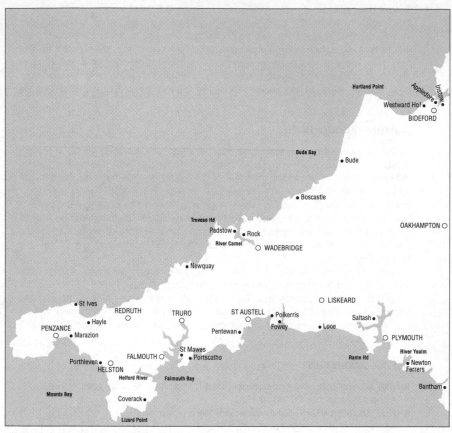

West Country: Severn to Swanage

Beachley Point - Car Ferry Slipway, Ferry Road

Type:	brick slipway under Severn Bridge
Suits:	all powered craft
Availability:	all states of tide
Restrictions:	site is subject to fierce tidal currents (up to 12 knots) and is only suitable for experienced boaters with adequately powerful craft
Facilities:	fuel nearby, parking for car and trailer on site, toilets nearby
Dues:	none
Charge:	none
Directions:	take A48 from Chepstow towards Gloucester, turning right after 1 mile following signs to Sedbury and Beachley: site is at end of road
Waters accessed:	Severn Estuary and Bristol Channel

Lydney Docks - Lydney Yacht Club, Harbour Road
Tel: (0291) 424134

Type:	concrete slipway
Suits:	sailing craft only
Availability:	approx. 1 hour either side HW with permission of Yacht Club
Restrictions:	site is subject to fierce tidal currents (up to 12 knots) and is only suitable for experienced boaters with adequately powered craft: access is via a narrow unmetalled road
Facilities:	no fuel, limited parking for car and trailer on site
Dues:	none
Charge:	yes
Directions:	from A48 follow signs to Lydney, then to the Industrial Estate and continue along Harbour Road to Docks
Waters accessed:	Severn Estuary and Bristol Channel

Bristol - Bristol Marina, Hanover Place
Tel: (0272) 213198

Type:	wide concrete into deep water of Floating Harbour
Suits:	all craft up to approx. 18' LOA
Availability:	all states of tide 0800-2200
Restrictions:	6 mph speed limit in harbour: pwc prohibited
Facilities:	diesel on site, petrol nearby, parking for car and trailer, toilets, chandlery, outboard repairs and full marina facilities on site
Dues:	approx £5.00
Charge:	no separate fee charged
Directions:	from city centre follow signs to "SS Great Britain" and Historic Harbour: access is via Cumberland Rd and Hanover Place
Waters accessed:	Severn Estuary, Bristol Channel and Kennet and Avon Canal

Bristol - Underfall Yard, Cumberland Road
Tel: (0272) 297608/264797 (Harbour Office)

Type:	concrete slipway into min 3' water in Floating Harbour
Suits:	all craft up to 18' LOA
Availability:	0800 -1700 (winter), 0800 - dusk (summer)
Restrictions:	6 mph speed limit in harbour, 4 mph in canal and river: water-skiing permitted at certain times, pwc prohibited
Facilities:	fuel nearby, parking for car and trailer on site, toilets, chandlery and outboard repairs nearby
Dues:	approx. £6.50
Charge:	no separate fee charged
Directions:	follow signs to dock area from city centre: access is via Cumberland Rd and through Underfall Yard
Waters accessed:	River Avon, Severn Estuary and Bristol Channel

Clevedon - Seafront

Type:	narrow concrete slipway
Suits:	dinghies and small powercraft
Availability:	approx. 5 hours either side HW
Restrictions:	speed limit inshore: water-skiing permitted offshore
Facilities:	fuel in town, parking for car and trailer(c), toilets
Dues:	none
Charge:	none
Directions:	leave M5 at junction 20: site is 50yds west of pier
Waters accessed:	Severn Estuary and Bristol Channel

Weston-Super-Mare - Knightstone Harbour Slip
Tel: (0934) 631701 (Harbour Master)

Type:	concrete slipway
Suits:	all craft
Availability:	approx. 2 hours either side of HW by prior arrangement
Restrictions:	5 mph speed limit in harbour between pier and Knightstone Point: no water-skiing in this area; contact local water-ski club
Facilities:	fuel in town, no parking for car and trailer nearby, toilets nearby
Dues:	none
Charge:	none
Directions:	leave M5 at junction 21 and take A370 to town centre, turning right at sea front: site is at north end of town near Knightstone Point and Marina Lake

Waters accessed: Severn Estuary and Bristol Channel

Weston-Super-Mare - Uphill Boat Centre, Uphill Wharf
Tel: (0934) 418617

Type:	concrete slipway
Suits:	craft up to 45' LOA
Availability:	approx. 2 hours either side HW from 0830 - 1730
Restrictions:	speed limit inshore: water skiing permitted in Weston Bay
Facilities:	diesel on site, petrol available nearby, parking for car and trailer on site; toilets, chandlery, outboard repairs, moorings, storage, accomodation and RYA instruction all available on site
Dues:	none
Charge:	approx. £3.80 inc. parking and use of amenity block
Directions:	follow A370 south through town, turning off to Uphill 100 yds past Uphill Garage

Waters accessed: River Axe and Bristol Channel

Burnham-on-Sea - South Esplanade
Tel: (0278) 7852

Type:	concrete and wooden slipway with 15cwt weight limit
Suits:	all craft
Availability:	approx. 2 hours either side HW: at LW currents are strong and there is a lot of mud
Restrictions:	8 knot speed limit: water-skiing permitted in designated area; narrow slipway gets very congested
Facilities:	fuel nearby, parking for car (c) and trailer nearby, toilets nearby
Dues:	none
Charge:	none: but permit required to use slipway is obtainable free from Tourist Information Centre
Directions:	leave M5 at junction 22 following signs to Burnham-on-Sea: site is at south end of Esplanade at the end of Pier St

Waters accessed: Rivers Parrett, Brue and Severn and Bridgwater Bay

Watchet - Harbour Slipway
Tel: (0984) 63126 (Harbour Master)

Type:	concrete slipway
Suits:	all craft up to 30' LOA
Availability:	approx. 3 hours either side HW
Restrictions:	5 mph speed limit: no water-skiing or jet skis; narrow access road
Facilities:	fuel (2 miles), parking for car and trailer in Market St (c), toilets and chandlery nearby ; local Boat Owners Assoc. has compound and welcomes visitors
Dues:	none
Charge:	approx. £1.25
Directions:	follow A39 from Bridgwater or A358 from Taunton to Williton, turning off to Watchet
Waters accessed:	Bristol Channel

Minehead - Harbour Slipway
Tel: (0643) 702566/704263 (Harbour Master)

Type:	concrete slipway onto sand
Suits:	craft up to 30' LOA
Availability:	approx. 3 hours either side HW
Restrictions:	5 mph speed limit: jet skis prohibited
Facilities:	fuel (½ mile), parking for car and trailer nearby (c), toilets and chandlers nearby; local Boat Owners Assoc. has compound and welcomes visitors
Dues:	none
Charge:	approx. £1.25
Directions:	follow A358 from Taunton to Williton then the A39
Waters accessed:	Bristol Channel

Watermouth - Watermouth Harbour

Type:	concrete slipway onto hard sand
Suits:	all craft
Availability:	all states of tide for dinghies, HW for larger craft
Restrictions:	3 knot speed limit in harbour, water-skiing permitted outside harbour, slipway is used to launch Lifeboat and must be kept clear at all times
Facilities:	fuel, parking for car and trailer nearby, visitor's moorings
Dues:	none
Charge:	approx. £3.00 per boat
Directions:	from Barnstaple follow A39, B3229 north then A399 west: harbour is 4 miles east of Ilfracombe, opposite Watermouth Castle
Waters accessed:	Bristol Channel

Ilfracombe - Harbour Slipway
Tel: (0271) 862108 (Harbour Master -Summer only)

Type:	steep concrete slipway onto hard sand
Suits:	all craft up to approx. 18' LOA
Availability:	approx. 3-4 hours either side HW
Restrictions:	5 knot speed limit in harbour: pwc prohibited; contact the Harbour Master before use in Summer, slipway is used to launch Lifeboat and must be kept clear at all times
Facilities:	diesel, parking for car and trailer (c), toilets all on site
Dues:	none
Charge:	none
Directions:	from Barnstaple follow A361 or signs from Blackmoor Gate
Waters accessed:	Bristol Channel

Instow - Instow Promenade
Tel: (0271) 861081 (Instow Marine Services - Harbour Master)

Type:	concrete slipway onto sand
Suits:	all craft
Availability:	approx. 3 hours either side HW
Restrictions:	7 knot speed limit in estuary: water-skiing in designated area
Facilities:	diesel on site, parking for car and trailer (c), assistance with launching, outboard repairs; chandlery and diving supplies in Northam
Dues:	none
Charge:	none
Directions:	from Barnstaple/Bideford follow A39: site is off road on east side of River Torridge
Waters accessed:	Taw and Torridge Estuaries and Bristol Channel

Bideford - Bank End Slipway
Tel: (0237) 477676 (Tourist Information Centre, Victoria Park)

Type:	concrete slipway onto soft mud
Suits:	all craft
Availability:	1½ hours either side HW
Restrictions:	7 knot speed limit in estuary: water-skiing in designated area
Facilities:	fuel from petrol station (200 yds), parking for car and trailer on site (c), toilets in Victoria Park (100 yds), chandlery and diving supplies at Northam
Dues:	none
Charge:	none
Directions:	follow A39 west from Barnstaple, turning left after crossing river: site is adjacent to Bideford Quay: access through car park
Waters accessed:	River Torridge and Bristol Channel

Appledore - Ferry Slip, Appledore Quay

Type:	concrete slipway onto firm mud
Suits:	small sailing or power craft only
Availability:	approx. 2 hours either side HW
Restrictions:	7 knot speed limit in estuary: water-skiing in designated area
Facilities:	no fuel, parking for car and trailer (200 yds) (c), toilets (100 yds), chandlery and diving facilities at Northam
Dues:	none
Charge:	none
Directions:	follow A39 to outskirts of Bideford: at Heywood Road roundabout take the A386 to Appledore; slipway on quayside
Waters accessed:	River Torridge and Bristol Channel

Appledore - Churchfields Slipway

Type:	concrete slipway
Suits:	all craft
Availability:	approx. 5 hours either side HW
Restrictions:	7 knot speed limit in estuary: water-skiing in designated area
Facilities:	fuel nearby, parking for car and trailer on site (c), toilets (50 yds), chandlery and diving supplies at Northam
Dues:	none
Charge:	none
Directions:	follow A 39 to outskirts of Bideford: at Heywood Road roundabout take the A386 to Appledore; site is in Churchfields Car Park at end of quay
Waters accessed:	River Torridge and Bristol Channel

Westward Ho! - Slipway

Type:	concrete slipway onto sand
Suits:	small craft which can be manhandlled only
Availability:	at all states of tide but launching may be difficult at HW due to heavy breaking seas
Restrictions:	7 knot speed limit in certain areas: before launching craft must be manhandled over large sandy beach
Facilities:	no fuel, parking for car and trailer on site (c), toilets in Golf Links Road (100 yds), chandlery and diving facilities at Northam
Dues:	none
Charge:	none
Directions:	follow A 39 to Bideford outskirts taking B3236 to Westward Ho! town centre: site is at end of Westbourne Terrace
Waters accessed:	Barnstaple Bay and Bristol Channel

Bude - Harbour Slipway
Tel: (0288) 353111 or (0208) 815073 (Harbour Master)

Type:	steep stone and concrete slipway
Suits:	all craft
Availability:	approx. 2 hours either side HW
Restrictions:	access is via a narrow road along the breakwater: jet skis are prohibited from this site and water-skiing is only permitted offshore: the use of this site is very dependent on sea and weather conditions - consult the Harbour Master before launching
Facilities:	fuel from garages in town, parking for car and trailer nearby (c 1st Apr-30th Sept), toilets nearby
Dues:	none
Charge:	approx. £20 pa
Directions:	follow A39 south from Barnstaple or B3254/A3072 from Launceston: site is near sea lock at entrance to Bude Canal
Waters accessed:	Bude Bay

Boscastle Harbour - Harbour Slip
Tel: (0840) 250453 (Harbour Master)

Type:	concrete slipway
Suits:	small powered craft and trailer-sailers
Availability:	approx. 1½ hours either side HW with Harbour Master's permission
Restrictions:	3 knot speed limit in harbour: speed boats prohibited but water-skiing is permitted offshore
Facilities:	fuel nearby, parking for car in car park nearby but trailers can be left in the boat park, toilets
Dues:	none
Charge:	approx. £3
Directions:	turn off the A39 onto the B3263: site is at head of harbour
Waters accessed:	Atlantic Ocean

Rock - Rock Sailing Club Slip, The Quay
Tel: (020 886) 2709

Type:	concrete slipway onto sandy beach
Suits:	all craft
Availability:	approx. 2 hours either side HW
Restrictions:	5 knot speed limit: water-skiing permitted in designated areas upstream; no parking on beach or slipway; busy in season
Facilities:	parking for car and trailer (c), toilets at SC, chandlery nearby
Dues:	approx. £2.10 (£10 per week)
Charge:	no separate fee charged
Directions:	from Bideford follow A39 to Wadebridge, turn onto B3314 then minor roads to Rock
Waters accessed:	Camel Estuary and Padstow Bay

Rock - Ferry Point Slip

Type:	small wooden slipway onto sandy beach
Suits:	small craft only
Availability:	approx. 2 hours either side HW
Restrictions:	5 knot speed limit: no vehicles on beach
Facilities:	parking for car and trailer, toilets and chandlery nearby
Dues:	approx. £2.10 (£10 per week)
Charge:	no separate fee charged
Directions:	from Bideford follow A39 to Wadebridge, turn onto B3314 then minor roads to Rock: access to site is through car park
Waters accessed:	Camel Estuary and Padstow Bay

Wadebridge - The Quay, off Eddystone Road
Tel: (0841) 532239 (Harbour Office)

Type:	concrete slipway
Suits:	all craft
Availability:	approx. 2 hours either side HW
Restrictions:	5 knot speed limit: water-skiing in designated areas
Facilities:	fuel in town, parking for car and trailer (c) and toilets nearby
Dues:	approx. £2.10 (£10 per week)
Charge:	no separate fee charged
Directions:	from Bideford or Bude follow A39 into town, cross the bridge and turn right into Eddystone Rd: site is on quay after about 350yds
Waters accessed:	Camel Estuary and Padstow Bay

Wadebridge - Trevilling Quay Road (Chapman and Hewitt)
Tel: (0208) 813487

Type:	concrete slipway
Suits:	all craft
Availability:	approx. 2 hours either side HW by prior arrangement
Restrictions:	speed limit: water-skiing permitted in designated areas
Facilities:	diesel and parking for car and trailer (c) on site, toilets nearby, chandlery, crane hire and all boatyard facilities
Dues:	approx. £2.10 (£10 per week)
Charge:	approx. £18
Directions:	from Bideford or Bude follow A39 into town: site is on west side of estuary
Waters accessed:	Camel Estuary and Padstow Bay

Padstow - Sailing Club Slip, West Quay (South Slip)
Tel: (0841) 532239 (Harbour Office)

Type:	steep and fairly narrow concrete slipway
Suits:	all craft up to approx. 17' LOA

Availability: approx. 3½ hours either side HW
Restrictions: speed limit: water-skiing is permitted in designated area upstream and pwc are regulated
Facilities: diesel on site, parking for car and trailer on site (c), toilets, chandlery and outboard repairs nearby
Dues: approx £2.10 (£10 per week)
Charge: no separate fee
Directions: follow A 39 from Bideford, then A389 west of Wadebridge: site is adjacent Harbour Office and access is through car park
Waters accessed: Camel Estuary and Padstow Bay

Padstow - Iron Horse Slip, North Quay (Half Tide Slip)
Tel: (0841) 532239 (Harbour Office)

Type: concrete slipway into Outer Basin
Suits: sailing dinghies and small powered craft
Availability: approx. 2.½ hours either side HW
Restrictions: access to site is from very congested road and through car park
Facilities: diesel nearby, parking for car and trailer nearby (c), toilets, chandlery and outboard repairs available nearby
Dues: approx. £2.10 (£10 per week)
Charge: no separate fee
Directions: follow A39 from Bideford, then A389 west of Wadebridge: access in Padstow is via difficult and narrow roads
Waters accessed: Camel Estuary and Padstow Bay

Newquay - Harbour Slip, South Quay Hill
Tel (0637) 872804 (Harbour Master)

Type: granite slipway onto beach
Suits: all craft
Availability: all states of tide across the beach but best 4 hours either side HW
Restrictions: 4 knot speed limit in and out of harbour: water-skiing allowed 400 m off beaches but pwc are prohibited;4-wheel drive vehicles are recommended for launching over beach and breaking waves can prevent launching: all boats should carry safety equipment and a safety briefing from the Harbour Master is required
Facilities: diesel on site, limited parking for car and trailer on site (c), toilets and chandlery nearby: boats cannot be left overnight
Dues: none
Charge: approx. £1.20
Directions: from A39 Bideford road take A3059, or A3058 from A30: site is NE of town and access can be very congested in summer
Waters accessed: Newquay Bay and Watergate Bay

St Ives - Lifeboat Slipway, Wharf Road
Tel: (0736) 795018 (Harbour Master)

Type:	(1) concrete (2) hard sandy beach
Suits:	all craft
Availability:	(1) approx 2½ hours either side HW (2) all states of tide
Restrictions:	5 knot speed limit: no water-skiing in harbour; concrete slip must be kept clear at all times for lifeboat, and harbour master to be contacted prior to use of (1)
Facilities:	fuel in town, parking for car and trailer in public car parks (c), toilets and chandlery nearby
Dues:	by engine size, approx. £2.60 per day (up to 10hp), £7.75 (over 10hp) or £23.50 (pwc)
Charge:	no separate fee charged
Directions:	take A3074 off A30 Penzance road; slipway is adjacent to the main road through the town
Waters accessed:	St Ives Bay

Penzance Harbour - Albert Pier Slipway
Tel (0736) 66113 (Harbour Office, Wharf Road)

Type:	concrete slipway
Suits:	all craft
Availability:	2-3 hours either side HW
Restrictions:	5 knot speed limit in harbour: water-skiing allowed offshore; pwc permitted provided speed limit in harbour is observed
Facilities:	diesel on site, petrol nearby, parking for car and trailer on site (c), toilets, chandlery and outboard repairs available nearby
Dues:	approx. £5.00
Charge:	none
Directions:	from A30, in town go past BR station then turn left past the Bus Station and site is 100m on right by the Sailing Club
Waters accessed:	Mounts Bay

Marazion

Type:	concrete slipway onto sand beach
Suits:	small craft which can be manhandled
Availability:	most states of tide
Restrictions:	speed limit
Facilities:	fuel nearby, parking for car and trailer (c), toilets in village
Dues:	none
Charge:	none
Directions:	from Penzance follow A30 east: site is close to causeway to St Michaels Mount
Waters accessed:	Mounts Bay

Porthleven - Quayside
Tel (0326) 561141

Type:	concrete slipway
Suits:	all craft
Availability:	approx. 3 hours either side HW
Restrictions:	3 mph speed limit in inner harbour, 5 mph in outer harbour: no water-skiing; harbour is primarily a fishing harbour and exposed in strong S to SW winds when launching is not permitted
Facilities:	fuel nearby, parking for car and trailer in nearby car park (c), toilets and chandlery nearby, other facilities in Falmouth
Dues:	included in launching fee
Charge:	approx. £4.70 inc. vat
Directions:	turn off A394 at Helston then take B3304 for 2 miles
Waters accessed:	Mounts Bay

Coverack - Harbour Slipway
Tel: (0326) 280583 Harbour Master

Type:	concrete slipway onto firm sand
Suits:	dinghies and small powercraft
Availability:	approx. 2-3 hours either side HW by arrangement with Harbour Master
Restrictions:	speed limit: pwc and water-skiing prohibited in harbour; site is sheltered in SW winds
Facilities:	no fuel, parking for car and trailer (c), toilets and outboard repairs
Dues:	approx £10.00
Charge:	no separate fee
Directions:	turn off A394 at Helston, taking the A3083 and then B3293/3294: site is on east side of Lizard peninsula
Waters accessed:	English Channel east of Lizard peninsula

Gillan Creek - St Anthony-in-Meneage
Tel: (0326) 231 357 (Sailaway St Anthony Ltd)

Type:	ramp onto beach
Suits:	craft up to 22' LOA
Availability:	approx. 3 hours either side HW from 0800-1800
Restrictions:	6 knot speed limit in creek: divers and jet skiers may not use this site; access roads are narrow and steep
Facilities:	diesel, parking for car and trailer (c), toilets and chandlery moorings, boat park; tractor assistance available during working hours
Dues:	none
Charge:	approx. £4
Directions:	from Helston take the A3083 then B3293 for St Keverne: turn left before Goonhilly Satellite Station for Helford following signs for St Anthony
Waters accessed:	Helford River and Falmouth Bay

Helford River - Gweek Quay Boatyard
Tel: 032 622 657

Type:	steep concrete slipway
Suits:	all craft with draught up to 7': crane to 14 tons
Availability:	2 hours either side HW: yard open 0900-1800, later by arrangement
Restrictions:	6 knot speed limit in river: water-skiing prohibited
Facilities:	diesel on site, petrol nearby, parking for car and trailer on site (c if longer than 12 hours), toilets, chandlery and all yard facilities, moorings and cafe, pub
Dues:	included in launching fee
Charge:	approx. £8.50: craneage £2.50 per foot
Directions:	from Helston, follow signs to the Lizard and St Keverne or the Seal Sanctuary, then to Gweek
Waters accessed:	Helford River and Falmouth Bay

Helford River - Port Navas

Type:	launching over hard shingle foreshore
Suits:	dinghies only
Availability:	approx. 2-3 hours either side HW
Restrictions:	speed limit in river: water-skiing prohibited; narrow and limited access
Facilities:	no fuel, very limited parking for car and trailer nearby
Dues:	none
Charge:	none
Directions:	from A394 (Penryn to Helston road) turn off in Mabe Burnthouse following signs to Mawnan Smith, then Constantine and Port Navas
Waters accessed:	Helford River and Falmouth Bay

Helford River - Helford Passage

Type:	launching over hard shingle
Suits:	dinghies only
Availability:	approx. 4 hours either side HW
Restrictions:	6 knot speed limit in river: water-skiing prohibited
Facilities:	no fuel, parking for car and trailer (c), toilets at pub
Dues:	none
Charge:	none
Directions:	from Falmouth follow minor roads to Mawnan Smith then signs for Helford Passage: site is in front of the 'Ferry Inn'
Waters accessed:	Helford River and Falmouth Bay

Falmouth - Grove Place Boat Park and Slipway
Tel: (0326) 312285 (Harbour Office, 44 Arwenack Street)

Type:	large slipway of brick and concrete blocks
Suits:	all craft
Availability:	all states of tide: 0900-1600 only in winter
Restrictions:	8 knot speed limit in harbour: water-skiing permitted in designated areas; jet-skis are not welcome
Facilities:	fuel nearby, car parking nearby (c), trailers can be left on site (c), chandlery, diving supplies and outboard repairs all available in town; boats can be stored ashore (c), watersports centre adjacent
Dues:	included in launching fee
Charge:	approx. £1.80 daily, £8.75 weekly and £21.75 annual
Directions:	follow A39 to town centre: site is off main street
Waters accessed:	Fal Estuary and Falmouth Bay

Falmouth - North Parade (Port Falmouth Boatyard)
Tel: (0326) 313248

Type:	concrete slipway
Suits:	all craft
Availability:	approx. 2 hours either side HW in working hours
Restrictions:	8 knot speed limit in harbour: water-skiing permitted in designated areas; use of slip by prior arrangement only
Facilities:	fuel nearby, parking for car and trailer, toilets, chandlery, diving supplies, outboard repairs nearby, crane on request
Dues:	none
Charge:	approx. £5.00
Directions:	from Truro follow A39 to Penryn: site is on North Parade just before marina
Waters accessed:	Fal Estuary, Penryn River and Falmouth Bay

Penryn - Church Slip
Tel: (0872) 72130/78131 (Harbour Office, Truro)

Type:	concrete and wooden slipway
Suits:	dinghies only
Availability:	approx. 2 hours either side HW by prior arrangement
Restrictions:	5 knot speed limit: pwc prohibited; narrow access
Facilities:	fuel nearby, parking for car only nearby, toilets , chandlery, diving supplies and outboard repairs all available nearby
Dues:	none
Charge:	none
Directions:	from Truro follow A39 to Falmouth: Penryn is at head of river and site is just below church off the Flushing road
Waters accessed:	Penryn River, Fal Estuary and Falmouth Bay

Flushing - Quayside

Type:	concrete slipway
Suits:	dinghies only
Availability:	approx. 2 hours either side HW
Restrictions:	5 knot speed limit: limited access
Facilities:	fuel in village, parking for car and trailer on quay (c)
Dues:	none
Charge:	none
Directions:	from Truro follow A39 to Falmouth turn off to Flushing in Penryn: site is opposite 'Seven Stars' pub
Waters accessed:	Penryn River, Fal Estuary and Falmouth Bay

Mylor - Mylor Yacht Harbour
Tel: (0326) 372121

Type:	concrete slipway
Suits:	all craft
Availability:	approx. 4 hours either side HW
Restrictions:	speed limit: check for availability before use
Facilities:	fuel, parking for car and trailer (c), toilets and showers, chandlery, travel hoist and restaurant
Dues:	none
Charge:	approx. £2
Directions:	from Truro follow A39 to Falmouth turning off to Mylor and follow minor roads to south side of Mylor Creek: site is close to church
Waters accessed:	Mylor Creek, Fal Estuary and Falmouth Bay

Feock - Loe Beach Boat Park
Tel: (0872) 864295 (Beach Cafe)

Type:	shingle foreshore
Suits:	small craft only
Availability:	all states of tide
Restrictions:	narrow access road
Facilities:	fuel from local garage, parking for car and trailer on site(c), toilets and cafe: all other facilities available in Falmouth or at marinas
Dues:	none
Charge:	none
Directions:	from Truro take the road to Feock and then follow signs
Waters accessed:	Fal Estuary and Falmouth Bay

Truro - Malpas Road, Sunny Corner
Tel: (0872) 72130 (Harbour Master)

Type:	steep right-angled concrete slipway onto muddy beach
Suits:	small powered craft, dinghies and small trailer-sailers

Availability:	approx. 2 hours either side HW by prior arrangement
Restrictions:	speed limit in harbour: jet skis prohibited but water-skiing permitted in designated areas
Facilities:	fuel nearby, limited parking for car only nearby, toilets, chandlery and other facilities in Truro
Dues:	none
Charge:	none
Directions:	turn left off A39 Truro bypass at roundabout following signs to Malpas
Waters accessed:	Truro River, Fal Estuary and Falmouth Bay

St Just-in-Roseland - Pasco & Son
Tel: (0326) 270269

Type:	concrete slipway
Suits:	all craft
Availability:	all states of tide
Restrictions:	5 knot speed limit: water-skiing permitted in designated area; check for availability, site can be busy in season
Facilities:	diesel, petrol nearby, parking for car and trailer nearby (c)
Dues:	none
Charge:	none
Directions:	from Truro follow B3289 via King Harry ferry: boatyard is adjacent to church
Waters accessed:	Percuil River, Fal Estuary and Falmouth Bay

St Mawes - Harbour Slipway
Tel: (0326) 270553 (Harbour Master)

Type:	steep concrete slipway
Suits:	craft up to 25' LOA
Availability:	approx. 1 hour either side HW (less at neaps) for direct launch but can be used longer if craft manhandled over beach; site available 0900-1630 Apr-Oct
Restrictions:	5 knot speed limit in harbour: water-skiing and jet skis prohibited; access to site is through narrow and very congested streets; slipway is steep with 90° turn at bottom if launching over beach, there are locked posts at slipway head so Hbr Mr must be contacted prior to launching
Facilities:	fuel from garage (1 mile), limited parking for car on quay(c) and for trailer in car park nearby (c) (both often full); visitors moorings are available from the Sailing Club Tel: (0326) 270686
Dues:	included in launch fee
Charge:	approx. £3.00
Directions:	from St Austell follow A390 west taking the B3287 signposted Roseland Peninsula then right onto A3078 to St Mawes: harbour is in centre of town
Waters accessed	Percuil River, Fal Estuary and Falmouth Bay

St Mawes - Stone Quay (St Mawes Sailing Club)
Tel (0326) 270686 or (0326) 270300 (Quay Secreatary)

Type:	concrete slipway onto soft mud
Suits:	dinghies and small powered craft up to 16' LOA
Availability:	all states of tide but very muddy at LW
Restrictions:	5 knot speed limit: site is private and permission to use must be obtained in advance; access is via a steep narrow lane with tight curves and there is a locked barrier with instructions for obtaining key displayed on quay notice board
Facilities:	parking for car and trailer nearby (c); temporary membership welcomed allowing access to all facilities during opening hours (all year 1000 to 1430 and additionally in season 1800 to 2300)
Dues:	none
Charge:	approx. £0.50 payable to club
Directions:	from St Austell follow A390 west taking the B3287 signposted Roseland Peninsula then right onto A3078 to St Mawes: access is down lane signed off Polvarth road approx ½ mile after garage
Waters accessed:	Percuil River, Fal Estuary and Falmouth Bay

St Mawes - Polvarth Boatyard (Hamling & Hitchings)
Tel: (0326) 270481

Type:	concrete slipway
Suits:	all craft up to 20' LOA
Availability:	approx. 4 hours either side HW during working hours
Restrictions:	5 knot speed limit: check for availability; access is via a steep narrow lane
Facilities:	fuel, parking for car and trailer (c)
Dues:	none
Charge:	yes
Directions:	from St Austell follow A390 west taking the B3287 signposted Roseland Peninsula then right onto A3078 to St Mawes:site is at end of Polvarth Lane and upstream of Polvarth Pt
Waters accessed:	Percuil River, Fal Estuary and Falmouth Bay

Percuil - Slipway

Type:	steep concrete slipway onto shingle beach
Suits:	dinghies and powerboats only
Availability:	most states of tide
Restrictions:	5 knot speed limit
Facilities:	no fuel, parking for car and trailer, toilets
Dues:	none
Charge:	none
Directions:	from St Austell follow A390 west taking the B3287 signposted Roseland Peninsula then right onto A3078 to Trewithian then follow minor roads; site is on east bank of river
Waters accessed:	Percuil River, Fal Estuary and Falmouth Bay

Type:	concrete slipway
Suits:	dinghies only
Availability:	approx. 4 hours either side of HW
Restrictions:	5 knot speed limit
Facilities:	no fuel, parking for car and trailer, boat park
Dues:	none
Charge:	none
Directions:	from St Austell follow A390 west taking the B3287 signposted Roseland Peninsula then right onto A3078 to Trewithian then follow minor roads to Gerrans and signs to Place

Waters accessed: Percuil River, Fal Estuary and Falmouth Bay

Portscatho - Harbour Slip
Tel: (0872) 580 616 (Harbour Master)

Type:	steep concrete and stone slipway onto sand
Suits:	shallow draught craft up to 17' LOA
Availability:	most states of tide by arrangement with Harbour Master
Restrictions:	5 mph speed limit in harbour and near beach: water-skiing permitted in designated areas
Facilities:	fuel nearby, parking for car and trailer nearby, toilets on site, chandlers, diving supplies and outboard repairs available nearby
Dues:	approx. £2
Charge:	no separate fee
Directions:	from St Austell follow A390 west taking the B3287 signposted Roseland Peninsula then right onto A3078 to Trewithian then follow minor roads to Portscatho

Waters accessed: Gerrans Bay

Pentewan - Pentewan Sands Holiday Park
Tel: (0726) 843485

Type:	concrete slipway
Suits:	all light craft
Availability:	all states of tide except LWS 0700-2100
Restrictions:	speed limit: use by prior arrangement for residents or season ticket holders only; all powered craft subject to site regulations
Facilities:	fuel nearby, parking for car and trailer, toilets, diving supplies nearby, hire of dinghies,canoes,wetsuits etc.
Dues:	none
Charge:	approx. £5.50 including parking
Directions:	from St Austell follow B3273 south towards Mevagissey: site is on left after approx. 4 miles

Waters accessed: St Austell Bay

St Austell - Porthpean Beach
Tel: (0726) 74466 extn 2248

Type:	very steep concrete slipway onto soft sandy beach
Suits:	dinghies and small powered craft
Availability:	all states of tide
Restrictions:	5 mph speed limit close to beach: pwc and water-skiing prohibited; 0900-1800 Easter to mid Sept launching prohibited for craft over 10hp; part of beach buoyed off for bathing only in summer; launching area heavily used by Porthpean SC; vehicles can only be used on beach for launching and retrieval purposes and beach is only suitable for 4-wheel drive off road vehicles
Facilities:	no fuel, parking for car and trailer nearby (c), toilets, Porthpean SC at top of slip; beach attendants on duty Easter-mid Sept
Dues:	none
Charge:	none
Directions:	from A 390 St Austell bypass approx. 300yds east of 'Asda' roundabout turn left onto minor road signposted Porthpean, then take 1st left after hospital to Porthpean beach

Waters accessed: St Austell Bay

Polkerris - Beach
Tel: (0726) 815142

Type:	
Suits:	all craft up to 18' LOA
Availability:	all states of tide
Restrictions:	speed limit in harbour: water-skiing allowed offshore but no beach starts; no launching of power craft 30hp and over on daily basis but moorings can be arranged for any powerboats; harbour exposed in SW gales, narrow access road
Facilities:	fuel nearby (1 mile), parking for car nearby (c), trailer on site , toilets, pub and cafe; chandlery and other facilities in Fowey (3 miles)
Dues:	none
Charge:	approx. £2.00 includes trailer parking
Directions:	from St Austell follow A390 east turning right in Par onto A3082 towards Fowey: site is down minor road to left signposted Polkerris and Beach

Waters accessed: St Austell Bay

Fowey - Caffa Mill Car/Dinghy Park
Tel: (0726) 74466 extn.2248 (Restormel Borough Council)

Type:	concrete slipway onto shingle
Suits:	sailing and powered craft up to 25' LOA
Availability:	all states of tide
Restrictions:	6 knot speed limit in harbour: water-skiing, windsurfers and jet skis prohibited in harbour; access to site is via narrow roads

Facilities: fuel nearby, parking for car and trailer on site for limited time (c), toilets on site, other facilities in town
Dues: none
Charge: approx. £1
Directions: follow signs from roundabout by 'Four Turnings' service station to Fowey Jetties or Bodinnick car ferry: these will lead to the Caffa Mill car park on the Fowey side of the river
Waters accessed: Fowey Harbour

Mixtow Pill - Slipway
Tel: (0726) 832471/2 (Harbour Office)

Type: concrete slipway approx. 8' wide
Suits: dinghies and very small power craft
Availability: approx. 1.½ hours either side HW
Restrictions: 6 knot speed limit in harbour: water-skiing, jet skis and windsurfers prohibited; access is via narrow one-way roads with sharp bends
Facilities: diesel nearby, no parking; other facilities in Fowey
Dues: none
Charge: none
Directions: turn off at Lostwithiel following signs to Lerryn, then St Veer and Mixtow
Waters accessed: Fowey Harbour

Bodinnick - Penmarlam Slip, Yeate Farm
Tel: (0726) 870256 (D.J. and A.M. Oliver)

Type: steep concrete slipway (1:6) onto hard beach
Suits: all craft
Availability: 0900 to dusk subject to tides and by prior arrangement
Restrictions: 6 knot speed limit in river: water-skiing, windsurfing and jet skis prohibited; narrow access
Facilities: fuel (4 miles), parking for car and trailer on site (c), toilets on site, chandlery and diving supplies (1 mile), outboard repairs (4 miles); small caravan site on farm, cottage to let, boats can be stored and tractor and hoist available up to 4 tons
Dues: none
Charge: approx. £1
Directions: from A38 Liskeard bypass, fork left at Dobwalls onto the A390: turn left at E Taphouse onto the B3359 and follow signs to the Bodinnick Ferry; farm is ½ mile east of ferry
Waters accessed: Fowey Harbour

Polruan Quay Slip

Tel: (0726) 832471/2 (Harbour Office)

Type:	wide concrete slipway onto beach
Suits:	dinghies and small powered craft only
Availability:	approx. 3 hours either side HW
Restrictions:	6 knot speed limit in harbour: water-skiing, windsurfers and jet skis prohibited; narrow access roads; area may be very congested
Facilities:	fuel on quay, no parking, toilets and chandlery in village
Dues:	none
Charge:	yes
Directions:	from Lostwithiel follow minor roads to Polruan
Waters accessed:	Fowey Harbour

West Looe - Millpool Boatyard (Norman Pearn & Co Ltd)

Tel (0503) 262244

Type:	concrete slipway
Suits:	all craft
Availability:	approx. 4 hours either side HW
Restrictions:	5 knot speed limit: water-skiing allowed in open sea; site is above bridge so not suitable for boats with masts
Facilities:	fuel nearby, parking for car and trailer on site (c), toilets nearby, chandlery, outboard repairs and all yard facilities available
Dues:	none
Charge:	approx. £4
Directions:	from Plymouth take the A38 then A387 following signs to Looe: cross bridge into W. Looe taking the second turning right, going down hill to mini roundabout then heading back towards Looe
Waters accessed:	Looe Harbour and Bay

West Looe - The Quay

Tel: (0503) 262839

Type:	concrete slipway
Suits:	all craft
Availability:	approx. 2½ hours either side HW
Restrictions:	5 knot speed limit in harbour and for some distance offshore: use by prior arrangement with Looe Harbour Commissioners
Facilities:	fuel nearby, parking for car and trailer nearby (c), toilets and showers nearby, chandlery, outboard repairs, diving supplies, moorings
Dues:	none
Charge:	approx. £1.50: weekly/monthly rates available
Directions:	from Plymouth take the A38 then A387 following signs to Looe: cross over bridge into W. Looe taking left turn to quay
Waters accessed:	Looe Harbour and Bay

Millendreath - Millendreath Holiday Village
Tel: (0503) 263281

Type: tractor launching
Suits: all craft except jet skis
Availability: all states of tide 0830-1800
Restrictions: 5 knot speed limit within 300m of beach
Facilities: fuel from Looe, parking for car and trailer on site (c), toilets, cafe, shop, pub, clubhouse: chandlery and outboard repairs in Looe
Dues: none
Charge: approx. £6
Directions: from Plymouth take the A38 then A387 following signs to Looe, turn left onto B3253 at Shorta Cross and follow signs
Waters accessed: Looe Bay

Downderry - Downderry Slipway

Type: concrete slipway
Suits: sailing dinghies, small powered craft and speedboats
Availability: 2 hours either side HW for direct launching but craft can be man-handled over the beach at all states of tide
Restrictions: narrow access:there is a voluntary code of conduct inshore
Facilities: no fuel or parking, toilets, shop and pub nearby
Dues: none
Charge: none
Directions: from Plymouth follow the A38, A374, A387 and B3247 then signs from village: site is 3 miles east of Looe
Waters accessed: Whitsand Bay

Portwrinkle - Harbour Slip

Type: concrete slipway
Suits: sailing dinghies, small powered craft and speedboats
Availability: at all states of tide or near HW for a direct launch
Restrictions: narrow access: there is a voluntary code of conduct inshore; site may be obstructed by lockable bollards - key with Harbour Master
Facilities: none
Dues: none
Charge: none
Directions: from Plymouth follow the A38/A374, then right onto B3247
Waters accessed: Whitsand Bay

Landrake
Tel: (0752) 851679 (Boating World)

Type:	concrete slipway
Suits:	all craft up to 40' LOA
Availability:	approx. 3 hours either side HW
Restrictions:	5 knot speed limit: water-skiing prohibited in harbour
Facilities:	diesel only, parking for car and trailer, toilets, chandlery, outboard repairs and cafe all on site
Dues:	none
Charge:	approx. £5.00
Directions:	from Plymouth follow A38 west to Landrake turning left when signposted 'Boating World' and following signs for 2 miles
Waters accessed:	Rivers Lynher, Tamar and St Germans and Plymouth Harbour

Torpoint - Southdown Marina, Southdown Quay, Millbrook
Tel (0752) 823084

Type:	launching over shingle hard
Suits:	all craft including sailboards and jet skis
Availability:	approx. 2 hours either side HW by prior arrangement
Restrictions:	10 knot speed limit in harbour: water-skiing prohibited in harbour: slipway must be booked in advance
Facilities:	diesel on site, petrol nearby, parking for car and trailer, toilets
Dues:	included in launching fee
Charge:	approx. £10
Directions:	from Plymouth take the A374 via the Torpoint ferry then the B3247 to Millbrook, or go along the A38 to Trerucefoot roundabout, taking the A374 onto the B3247 and turning off to Millbrook
Waters accessed:	River Tamar, Plymouth Harbour and Sound

Torpoint - Torpoint Yacht Harbour Ltd

Type:	shingle hard
Suits:	all craft
Availability:	approx, 3 hours either side HW
Restrictions:	10 knot speed limit in harbour: water-skiing prohibited in harbour:
Facilities:	diesel, petrol from garage, parking for car nearby, no parking for trailer, no toilets, chandlery
Dues:	none
Charge:	none
Directions:	from Plymouth follow A374 via Torpoint Ferry and then signs to Ballast Quay
Waters accessed:	River Tamar, Plymouth Harbour and Sound

Saltash - Jubilee Green and Waterside

Type: concrete slipway
Suits: all craft
Availability: approx. 2 hours either side HW for direct launch
Restrictions: 10 knot speed limit in harbour: water-skiing prohibited in harbour
Facilities: fuel nearby, parking for car and trailer nearby (c), toilets, pubs and club nearby
Dues: none
Charge: none
Directions: from Plymouth follow the A38 to Saltash
Waters accessed: River Tamar, Plymouth Harbour and Sound

Cargreen - Old Ferry Slip

Type: concrete slipway
Suits: sailing dinghies and small powered craft
Availability: approx. 2 hours either side HW
Restrictions: 10 knot speed limit in harbour: water-skiing prohibited in harbour; narrow access road
Facilities. no fuel, parking for car and trailer on site, toilets nearby, pub and shops
Dues: none
Charge: none
Directions: turn off A388 Saltash to Callington road following signs: site is in village close to the Spaniard Inn
Waters accessed: River Tamar, Plymouth Harbour and Sound

Calstock - Riverside

Type: concrete slipway
Suits: craft up to 20' LOA
Availability: approx. 1 hour either side HW
Restrictions: 10 knot speed limit in harbour: water-skiing prohibited in harbour; access to site is narrow and steep
Facilities: no fuel, parking (often congested) for car and trailer on site (c), toilets, pubs and shops
Dues: none
Charge: none
Directions: follow signs from the A390 Liskeard to Tavistock road
Waters accessed: River Tamar - upper navigable reaches and Plymouth Harbour

Bere Alston - Weir Quay Boatyard, Herons' Reach

Tel: (0822) 840474

Type:	concrete slipway
Suits:	all craft: facilities for launching boats up to 12 tons
Availability:	all states of tide by prior arrangement
Restrictions:	10 knot speed limit in harbour: water-skiing permitted in designated zone: phone in advance to advise arrival and requirements
Facilities:	diesel on site, petrol nearby, parking for car and trailer on site (c if for more than 24 hrs), toilets and showers, chandlery, storage ashore, moorings and all yard facilities
Dues:	none
Charge:	approx. £3 (dinghy) or £6 (trailer-sailer): others £2.95/ ft
Directions:	from Tavistock, take the A390 Liskeard road, turning left at the Harvest Home pub for Bere Alston: once in the village, take the lane to Weir Quay, turning left at the river
Waters accessed:	River Tamar and Plymouth Harbour and Sound

Plymouth - Richmond Walk

Tel: (0752) 556633

Type:	concrete slipway
Suits:	all craft
Availability:	all times except LW springs
Restrictions:	10 knot speed limit in harbour: water-skiing permitted in designated area; access road sometimes congested
Facilities:	fuel from marina adjacent, parking for car and trailer on site or at marina (c), toilets on site, all other facilities at marina
Dues:	none
Charge:	none
Directions:	head through Plymouth city centre, down Union St and straight over at Stonehouse roundabout (in the direction of the Torpoint ferry) taking the first left into Richmond Walk: site is adjacent the Mayflower Marina
Waters accessed:	River Tamar and Plymouth Harbour and Sound

Plymouth - Harbour Marine, Sutton Harbour

Tel: (0752) 666330

Type:	concrete slipway
Suits:	all craft
Availability:	at all states of tide into locked basin by prior arrangement only
Restrictions:	10 knot speed limit in harbour: water-skiing permitted in designated area
Facilities:	limited parking (c), toilets, chandlers and yard services on site
Dues:	none
Charge:	yes
Directions:	from east follow signs to city centre: at A374 (Exeter St) turn left

into Sutton Rd and look for slipway on harbour side

Waters accessed: River Tamar

Coxside - Queen Anne's Battery Marina
Tel: (0752) 671142

Type:	large concrete slipway
Suits:	all craft up to 30' LOA
Availability:	all states of tide
Restrictions:	10 knot speed limit in harbour: locked barriers across access 2400 to 0600; anyone entering the marina must report to the office
Facilities:	fuel on site, parking for car and trailer on site (c), toilets, chandlery, diving supplies, outboard repairs, sail repairs and many other facilities available at marina
Dues:	included in launching fee
Charge:	approx. £6
Directions:	from the A38, follow signs to the city centre and then to Coxside
Waters accessed:	Plymouth Sound

Newton Ferrers - Bridgend Quay
Tel: (0752) 072533 (Harbour Master)

Type:	concrete slipway into deep sheltered waters
Suits:	all craft
Availability:	approx. 2½ hours either side HW
Restrictions:	6 knot speed limit in harbour: no water-skiing
Facilities:	fuel nearby, limited parking for car and trailer (c), toilets nearby
Dues:	none
Charge:	none
Directions:	from Kingsbridge follow A379 towards Plymouth; turn onto B3186: site is at head of creek
Waters accessed:	Newton Creek and River Yealm

Bantham
Tel: (0548) 560593 (Harbour Master)

Type:	steep stone slipway; 4-wheel drive vehicles necessary
Suits:	dinghies and small powered craft
Availability:	approx. 2 hours either side HW by prior arrangement
Restrictions:	speed limit in harbour: water-skiing prohibited; beware strong tidal currents in river entrance; slip can be blocked by parked cars
Facilities:	parking for car and trailer nearby (c), pub 'The Sloop' nearby
Dues:	none
Charge:	none
Directions:	from Kingsbridge follow A379 towards Plymouth; turn left to Thurlestone Sands and thence to Bantham
Waters accessed:	River Avon and Bigbury Bay

Hope Cove - Inner Hope
Tel: (0548) 561500

Type: concrete slipway
Suits: all craft
Availability: all states of tide 0900-1800
Restrictions: speed limit inshore of buoys: water-skiing permitted offshore
Facilities: no fuel, parking for car and trailer (c) and toilets on site; boats can be parked by arrangement; Harbour Master on duty Easter to Sept
Dues: none
Charge: approx. £3.50, £12 per week, £30 per year (1993 rates)
Directions: from A38 (Exeter-Plymouth road) take the A384 to Totnes then A381 to Malborough via Kingsbridge: turn right and follow minor roads to Hope Cove: site is old lifeboat slip at Inner Hope
Waters accessed: Hope Cove and Bigbury Bay

South Sands
Tel: (0548) 843791 (Harbour Office, Whitestrand)

Type: short concrete slipway onto firm sand
Suits: all craft up to 18' LOA except jet skis
Availability: all states of tide
Restrictions: 8 knot speed limit: jet skis and water-skiing prohibited; access is across beach so 4-wheel drive recommended
Facilities: no fuel, parking for car and trailer nearby (c), toilets on site, moorings up to 20' LOA, all other facilities available in Salcombe
Dues: approx. £12 for 1 month (min. period available)
Charge: no separate fee
Directions: from A38 (Exeter-Plymouth road) take the A384 to Totnes then A381 to Salcombe via Kingsbridge: site is 1 mile south of town centre on south side of beach
Waters accessed: Salcombe Harbour

Salcombe - Whitestrand Quay
Tel: (0548) 843791 (Harbour Office, Whitestrand)

Type: concrete slipway onto shingle
Suits: small powered craft and sailing dinghies
Availability: approx. 3 hours either side HW for direct launch or at all states of tide over shingle
Restrictions: 8 knot speed limit in harbour: pwc, diving and water-skiing prohibited: access is narrow and congested (Batson Park slipway is best)
Facilities: fuel nearby, parking for car and trailer nearby(c), toilets on site, most other facilities available in town
Dues: approx £12 for 1 month (min. period available)
Charge: no separate fee
Directions: from A38, take the A384 to Totnes then A381 to Salcombe via Kingsbridge: site is in car park in centre of town
Waters accessed: Salcombe Harbour

Salcombe - Batson Creek Boat Park Slip, Gould Road
Tel: (0548) 843791 (Harbour Office, Whitestrand)

Type:	large concrete slipway onto shingle foreshore
Suits:	all craft except jet skis
Availability:	most states of tide
Restrictions:	8 knot speed limit: water-skiing, jet-skis and diving prohibited
Facilities:	fuel nearby, parking for car nearby and for trailer on site (c), toilets and other facilities nearby; 15 ton crane on site Tel:(0548) 843580
Dues:	approx. £12 for 1 month (min. period available)
Charge:	no separate fee
Directions:	from A38, take the A384 to Totnes then A381 to Salcombe via Kingsbridge: site is in Batson car park to north of town centre

Waters accessed: Salcombe Harbour

Kingsbridge - Squares Slip
Tel: (0548) 843791 (Harbour Office, Whitestrand)

Type:	concrete slipway
Suits:	all craft except jet skis
Availability:	2 hours either side HW or at HW for larger craft (up to 5' draught)
Restrictions:	8 knot speed limit in harbour: water-skiing, jet skis and diving prohibited; 15 ton weight limit and no parking on slipway
Facilities:	no diesel, petrol nearby, parking for car and trailer in car park adjacent (c), toilets and other facilities available nearby
Dues:	approx. £12 for 1 month (min. period available),
Charge:	no additional fee
Directions:	from A38 (Exeter-Plymouth road) take the A384 to Totnes then A381 to Kingsbridge: site is at Squares Quay at head of estuary

Waters accessed: Salcombe Harbour

Dartmouth - Higher Ferry Slip (South Side)
Tel: (0803) 832337 (Harbour Office)

Type:	concrete slipway
Suits:	all craft
Availability:	all states of tide
Restrictions:	6 knot speed limit in river: water-skiing prohibited
Facilities:	diesel on site, petrol nearby, parking for car and trailer nearby (c)
Dues:	approx. £2.12
Charge:	no separate fee
Directions:	from A38 (Exeter-Plymouth road) take the A384 following signs to Totnes turn onto A381 and at Halwell take the A3122 to Dartmouth: then follow signs to ferry

Waters accessed: River Dart and Start Bay

Dartmouth - Dart Marina, Sandquay

Tel: (0803) 833351

Type:	concrete slipway
Suits:	all craft except jet skis
Availability:	all states of tide
Restrictions:	6 knot speed limit in river: water-skiing and diving prohibited
Facilities:	diesel, parking for car and trailer, toilets, chandlery and all facilities
Dues:	approx. £2.12
Charge:	approx. £10
Directions:	from A38 (Exeter-Plymouth road) take the A384 following signs to Totnes turn onto A381 and at Halwell take the A3122 to Dartmouth: then follow signs to higher ferry: site is just north of ferry adjacent Dart Marina Hotel

Waters accessed: River Dart and Start Bay

Dittisham - Ham Car Park

Tel: (0803) 832337 (Harbour Office)

Type:	shingle foreshore
Suits:	small craft only
Availability:	near HW: launching difficult at neaps
Restrictions:	6 knot speed limit in river: water-skiing prohibited; access is via narrow congested roads and steep hill
Facilities:	no fuel, parking for car and trailer on site (c), toilets
Dues:	approx. £2.12
Charge:	no separate fee
Directions:	from A38 take the A384 following signs to Totnes, turning onto the A381and the A3122 to Dartmouth: follow signs to Dittisham

Waters accessed: River Dart and Start Bay

Totnes - Ashford Slip, Mill Tail (off The Plains)

Tel: (0803) 832337 (Dart Harbour Authority)

Type:	concrete slipway
Suits:	all craft
Availability:	approx. 3 hours either side HW
Restrictions:	6 knot speed limit in river: water-skiing prohibited
Facilities:	fuel nearby, parking for car and trailer in public car park nearby (c), toilets, chandlery nearby
Dues:	approx. £2.12
Charge:	none
Directions:	from A38 take the A384 following signs to Totnes

Waters accessed: River Dart and Start Bay

Totnes - Longmarsh (Steamer Quay)

Type:	concrete slipway
Suits:	sailing dinghies and small powered craft
Availability:	approx. 2 hours either side HW
Restrictions:	6 knot speed limit in harbour: water-skiing prohibited
Facilities:	no fuel, parking for car on site and for trailer nearby (c)
Dues:	approx. £2.12
Charge:	no separate fee
Directions:	from Exeter follow A38 turning off onto A384/A385: site is in town centre on east bank of river approx. ½ mile south of the town bridge
Waters accessed:	River Dart and Start Bay

Stoke Gabriel
Tel: (0803) 832337 (Harbour Office)

Type:	concrete slipway onto shingle
Suits:	sailing dinghies and small powered craft
Availability:	3 hours either side HW at springs, 2 hours either side at neaps
Restrictions:	6 knot speed limit in river: water-skiing prohibited; narrow access
Facilities:	fuel nearby, limited parking for car but not trailer on site (c), toilets
Dues:	approx. £2.12
Charge:	no additional fee
Directions:	from Exeter follow A38 turning off onto A384/A385 to Totnes; turn right after town and follow signs to Stoke Gabriel
Waters accessed:	River Dart and Start Bay

Galmpton Creek - Dartside Boatyard
Tel: (0803) 845445

Type:	concrete slipway
Suits:	dinghies and small powered craft
Availability:	approx. 2-3 hours either side HW during working hours
Restrictions:	6 knot speed limit in river: water-skiing prohibited; use of site by prior arrangement only; cars with trailers only, no commercial vehicles through village
Facilities:	limited parking for car and trailer, toilets, chandlery, diving supplies, outboard repairs all on site
Dues:	approx.£2.12
Charge:	approx. £7
Directions:	from Exeter follow A38 turning off onto A384/A385 to Totnes, then take A3022 towards Brixham and turn right in Galmpton village
Waters accessed:	River Dart and Start Bay

Greenway Quay
Tel: (0803) 844010

Type:	concrete slipway
Suits:	all craft
Availability:	approx. 4 hours either side HW
Restrictions:	6 knot speed limit in river: water-skiing prohibited; narrow access
Facilities:	parking for car and trailer on site (c)
Dues:	approx. £2.12
Charge:	approx. £5
Directions:	follow A3022 from Paignton, turning right at Galmpton: site is opposite Dittisham Ferry

Waters accessed: River Dart and Start Bay

Kingswear
Tel: (0803) 832337 (Harbour Office)

Type:	cobbled stone slipway
Suits:	dinghies and small powered craft up to 16' LOA
Availability:	approx. 4 hours either side HW
Restrictions:	6 knot speed limit in river: water-skiing prohibited; steep no through road leading to Lower Ferry often with queue of vehicles
Facilities:	no fuel, parking for car and trailer nearby (c), toilets, chandlery and outboard repairs all available in nearby marina
Dues:	approx. £2.12
Charge:	approx. £3
Directions:	from Exeter follow A38/A380 towards Torbay, turn onto A3022 and then right onto A379: take B3205 to Kingswear and Dartmouth ferry: site is close to ferry landing and Royal Dart YC

Waters accessed: River Dart and Start Bay

Brixham Harbour - Breakwater Slipway
Tel: (0803) 353321 (Harbour Master)

Type:	concrete slipway
Suits:	all craft
Availability:	all states of tide
Restrictions:	5 knot speed limit: water-skiing prohibited in harbour
Facilities:	fuel from garage nearby, parking for car and trailer nearby (c), toilets, chandlery in nearby marina, diving supplies and outboard repairs nearby
Dues:	none
Charge:	approx. £4
Directions:	from Exeter follow A38/A380 towards Torbay, then A3022 to Brixham Harbour

Waters accessed: Tor Bay

Brixham Harbour - Freshwater Quarry
Tel: (0803) 853321 (Harbour Master)

Type: concrete slipway
Suits: all craft
Availability: all states of tide
Restrictions: 5 knot speed limit: water-skiing prohibited in harbour
Facilities: fuel from garage nearby, parking for car and trailer nearby (c), toilets, chandlery in nearby marina, diving supplies and outboard repairs nearby
Dues: none
Charge: approx. £4
Directions: from Exeter follow A38/A380 towards Torbay, then A3022 to Brixham Harbour
Waters accessed: Tor Bay

Brixham Harbour - Oxen Cove
Tel: (0803) 853321 (Harbour Master)

Type: concrete slipway
Suits: all craft up to 20' LOA
Availability: all states of tide
Restrictions: 5 knot speed limit: water-skiing prohibited in harbour
Facilities: fuel from garage nearby, parking for car and trailer nearby (c), toilets, chandlery in nearby marina, diving supplies and outboard repairs nearby
Dues: none
Charge: approx. £4
Directions: from Exeter follow A38/A380 towards Torbay, then A3022 to Brixham Harbour
Waters accessed: Tor Bay

Paignton - Harbour Slip
Tel: (0803) 557812 (summer months only)

Type: concrete slipway onto hard sand
Suits: all craft up to 24' LOA
Availability: all states of tide
Restrictions: 5 knot speed limit inshore: water-skiing permitted in designated areas; fairly narrow access
Facilities: fuel nearby, parking for trailer on site and for car nearby, toilets, chandlery, diving supplies and outboard repairs all on site
Dues: included in launching fee
Charge: approx. £4.41
Directions: follow signs from town centre to south side of harbour
Waters accessed: Tor Bay

Torquay Harbour - Beacon Quay
Tel: (0803) 292429 (Harbour Master)

Type:	two fairly steep concrete slipways with slippery wooden ends
Suits:	small craft only
Availability:	all times except 1 hour either side LWS
Restrictions:	5 knot speed limit in harbour and near beaches: water-skiing permitted in designated areas, jet-skis permitted but restricted
Facilities:	fuel, parking for car and trailer(c), toilets (summer only), chandlery and outboard repairs all on site and diving supplies nearby
Dues:	included in launching fee
Charge:	approx. £4.41
Directions:	from Exeter follow A38/A380 towards Torbay, follow signs from town centre: site is adjacent Torquay Marina
Waters accessed:	Tor Bay

Babbacombe Beach
Tel: (0803) 292429 (Harbour Master)

Type:	concrete slipway onto sandy but rocky beach
Suits:	sailing dinghies and small powered craft only
Availability:	all states of tide (May to Sept only): notify Beach Master on site before launching
Restrictions:	5 knot speed limit inshore: water-skiing and jet skis prohibited; steep one-way single lane access
Facilities:	no fuel, limited parking for car only
Dues:	included in launching fee
Charge:	approx. £4.41
Directions:	follow A379 from Exeter and B3199 turning off to beach
Waters accessed:	Babbacombe Bay

Shaldon, Teignmouth - Albion Street
Tel: (0626) 773165

Type:	concrete slipway onto shingle
Suits:	all craft up to 20' LOA
Availability:	approx. 2 hours either side HW
Restrictions:	speed limit: water-skiing prohibited
Facilities:	fuel, parking for car and trailer nearby (c), toilets nearby, chandlery, diving supplies, outboard repairs
Dues:	none
Charge:	none
Directions:	from Exeter follow A38/A380 towards Torbay, turning left onto A381 to Teignmouth then right across bridge to Shaldon Fore St and turn left into Albion St
Waters accessed:	Teign Estuary and Babbacombe Bay

Combeinteignhead - Coombe Cellars
Tel: (0626) 773165

Type:	concrete slipway
Suits:	dinghies and small powered craft
Availability:	approx. 2 hours either side HW
Restrictions:	speed limit: for water-skiing contact South Devon Water-Ski Club, (see next entry)
Facilities:	parking for car and trailer (c), toilets, chandlery, diving supplies and outboard repairs nearby
Dues:	none
Charge:	none
Directions:	from Exeter follow A38/A380 towards Torbay, turning left onto A381 to Teignmouth then right across bridge to Shaldon; turn immediate right and follow river to Coombe Cellars: site is near Coombe Cellars Inn

Waters accessed: Teign Estuary and Babbacombe Bay

Teignmouth - Polly Steps Car Park
Tel: (0626) 773165 (Harbour Master)

Type:	concrete slipway
Suits:	all craft
Availability:	all states of tide
Restrictions:	10 mph speed limit in estuary and river and 5 knot speed limit within area marked by yellow buoys off beaches: water-skiing in estuary is prohibited but permitted in river only for members of the South Devon Water Sports Club (contact Dave or Barbara Hawkins Tel: Shaldon 873744 for temporary membership); owners/users of all powered craft launching at this site must produce documentary evidence of public liability insurance cover for £1m
Facilities:	fuel nearby, parking for car and trailer on site (c), toilets, chandlery and outboard repairs nearby: this is the best site in Teignmouth
Dues:	none
Charge:	approx. £5 incl parking
Directions:	from Exeter follow A379 to Teignmouth town centre and follow signs to Quays along roadway beside railway line: site is on west side of docks

Waters accessed: Teign Estuary and Babbacombe Bay

Teignmouth - Gales Hill Slipway
Tel: (0626) 773165 (Harbour Master)

Type:	launching over shingle hard
Suits:	all craft up to approx. 16' LOA
Availability:	all states of tide
Restrictions:	10 knot speed limit: water-skiing prohibited in estuary (see previous entry for details of water-skiing facility)

Facilities:	fuel nearby, parking for car and trailer nearby (c), toilets nearby, chandlery etc from Shaldon
Dues:	none
Charge:	none
Directions:	from Exeter follow A379 to Teignmouth town centre, site is adjacent to quay
Waters accessed:	River Teign and Babbacombe Bay

Exmouth - Orcombe Point Slipway, Queen's Drive

Type:	concrete slipway onto sand
Suits:	sailing dinghies, small powered craft and jet skis
Availability:	all states of tide
Restrictions:	10 knot speed limit in river: this is the only authorised launching site for jet skis
Facilities:	parking for car and trailer in car park nearby, other facilities in town
Dues:	none
Charge:	none
Directions:	from Exeter take A376 to Exmouth then signs to seafront: site is at the eastern end of the Esplanade
Waters accessed:	River Exe and Lyme Bay

Exmouth - Imperial Recreation Ground

Type:	concrete slipway
Suits:	sailing craft only
Availability:	approx. 1 hour either side HW
Restrictions:	10 knot speed limit in river: no jet skis or speed boats permitted to launch from this site
Facilities:	fuel, parking for car and trailer, toilets, most other facilities in town
Dues:	none
Charge:	none
Directions:	leave M5 at junction 30 following A376: access is via Royal Avenue
Waters accessed:	River Exe and Lyme Bay

Exmouth - Mamhead Slipway

Type:	steep concrete slipway with steel ramp onto sandy beach
Suits:	sailing craft only
Availability:	all states of tide
Restrictions:	10 knot speed limit in river: jet-skis and speed boats are prohibited at this site; site can be congested
Facilities:	fuel nearby, no parking for car or trailer, toilets nearby, chandlers and other facilities in town
Dues:	none
Charge:	none

Directions: leave M5 at junction 30 following A376: site is at west end of Esplanade near pier
Waters accessed: River Exe and Lyme Bay

Exmouth - Carlton Slipway

Type: launching across shingle beach
Suits: sailing craft only
Availability: all states of tide if craft manhandled across beach
Restrictions: 10 knot speed limit in river: jet skis and powerboats prohibited at this site
Facilities: no fuel, parking for car and trailer, toilets, chandlers nearby
Dues: none
Charge: none
Directions: leave M5 at junction 30 following A376: site is on Esplanade
Waters accessed: River Exe and Lyme Bay

Lympstone - Sowden End

Type: stone slipway
Suits: dinghies and sailboards
Availability: approx. 3 hours either side HW
Restrictions: 10 knot speed limit in river: jet skis and powerboats prohibited
Facilities: no fuel, parking for car and trailer nearby (c)
Dues: none
Charge: none
Directions: leave M5 at junction 30 following A376 towards Exmouth turning off right to Lympstone: access is via Sowden Lane
Waters accessed: River Exe and Lyme Bay

Budleigh Salterton - Ladram Bay Holiday Centre
Tel: (0395) 568398

Type: concrete slipway
Suits: dinghies and small powered craft up to 16' LOA
Availability: all states of tide by prior arrangement
Restrictions: 5 knot speed limit within 200m of shore: water-skiing permitted off-shore; cars not permitted to drive through caravan park after 1000
Facilities: no fuel, parking for car and trailer (c) and toilets on site
Dues: none
Charge: approx. £10 per day, £30 per week season tickets available
Directions: leave M5 at junction 30 following A3052 to Sidmout; turn left at Newton Poppleford and follow signs to Ladram Bay
Waters accessed: Lyme Bay

Axmouth Harbour - Seaton Marine Services
Tel: (0297) 23344

Type:	concrete slipway into river north of bridge
Suits:	sailing dinghies, small powered craft and jet skis
Availability:	approx. 3 hours either side HW by prior arrangement
Restrictions:	8 knot speed limit inshore: water-skiing permitted outside limits; entrance to river is very tricky, especially in onshore winds and should only be attempted within 2.½ hours HW
Facilities:	fuel nearby, parking for car and trailer on site (c), toilets and showers, chandlery, diving supplies and outboard repairs all on site
Dues:	none
Charge:	approx. £5
Directions:	follow A3052 from Exeter to Seaton: site is adjacent bridge on west side of river
Waters accessed:	River Axe and Lyme Bay

Lyme Regis - The Cobb
Tel: (0297) 442137 (Harbour Master)

Type:	wood and steel slipway
Suits:	small powered craft and sailing dinghies: launching can be awkward for trailer-sailers
Availability:	all states of tide
Restrictions:	dead slow speed in harbour: pwc prohibited; power boats must follow special instructions; access is via a very steep hill
Facilities:	fuel (2 miles), parking for car and trailer on site (c), toilets , chandlery and outboard repairs on site, diving supplies available nearby
Dues:	£5
Charge:	no separate fee
Directions:	follow A35 west from Dorchester and A3052 to Lyme Regis
Waters accessed:	Lyme Bay

Bridport Harbour - East Basin
Tel: (0308) 423222 (Harbour Master)

Type:	steep concrete slipway onto wood with 3 tonne weight limit
Suits:	all craft
Availability:	approx. 3 hours either side HW
Restrictions:	8 knot speed limit: water-skiing permitted 200m from shore but pwc prohibited; slipway is closed by gates during bad weather
Facilities:	fuel (200m), parking for car nearby (c) and for trailers on site, toilets, chandlery, diving supplies, shops and cafe nearby
Dues:	none
Charge:	approx. £5
Directions:	follow A35 west from Dorchester or East from Honiton: at Bridport bypass if westbound take 2nd exit at Crown roundabout, if eastbound take 4th exit at Crown roundabout
Waters accessed:	Lyme Bay

Weymouth Harbour - Commercial Road Quay
Tel: (0305) 206423 (Harbour Master)

Type:	concrete slipway
Suits:	craft up to 22' LOA
Availability:	all states of tide
Restrictions:	speed limit in harbour: windsurfers, water-skiing and jet skis prohibited in harbour
Facilities:	diesel nearby, parking for car nearby (c), and for trailer on site, all other facilities available nearby
Dues:	approx. £8 inc. trailer parking
Charge:	no separate fee
Directions:	from Esplanade roundabout at clock tower, turn right into King St, then left at the bottom, turning into Commercial Rd at the next roundabout: site is opposite muti-storey car park
Waters accessed:	Weymouth Bay

Weymouth - Weymouth Sailing Centre, Old Castle Road
Tel: (0305) 776549

Type:	two concrete slipways
Suits:	all craft except jet skis
Availability:	all states of tide except LWS
Restrictions:	6 knot speed limit inshore: jet skis prohibited in harbour; visitors must register on arrival
Facilities:	parking for car and trailer, toilets and showers and clubhouse
Dues:	none
Charge:	approx. £10 incl parking and use of club facilities for day
Directions:	follow signs to Portland from Weymouth, turning left into Old Castle Road and following signs to Sandsfoot Beach
Waters accessed:	Portland Harbour and Weymouth Bay

Peveril Point, Swanage - Peveril Boat Park
Tel: (0929) 422885

Type:	concrete slipway with winch
Suits:	all craft
Availability:	all states of tide
Restrictions:	speed limit inshore: water-skiing permitted offshore
Facilities:	fuel nearby, parking for car and trailer(c) and toilets on site, zchandlery, diving supplies and outboard repairs all available in town
Dues:	none
Charge:	approx. £10 inc parking or £5 launching only
Directions:	from Poole take A35 and A351 to Swanage and follow signs from High St
Waters accessed:	Swanage Bay and Durlston Bay

South Coast:
Studland to North Foreland

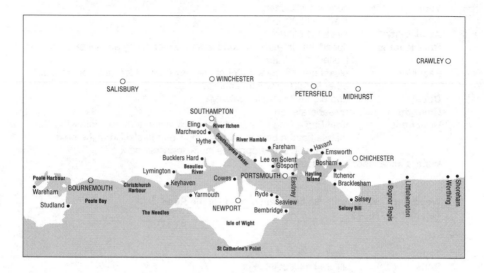

Studland - Shell Bay Marine & Watersports Centre, Ferry Road
Tel: (0929) 44 340

Type:	concrete slipway and hoist
Suits:	all craft
Availability:	approx. 4 hours either side HW
Restrictions:	speed limit within yellow marker buoys: pwc prohibited; access can be congested and booking is advisable at peak times
Facilities:	fuel nearby, parking for car and trailer on site, toilets, chandlery and outboard repairs on site, cafe, moorings storage; RYA recognised teaching establishment
Dues:	approx. £1.50 (only for craft with over 4 hp engine)
Charge:	approx. £12.50 (self-launching) or £22.50 (tractor assisted)
Directions:	leave Poole on A351 to Swanage turning off to Studland on B3351: access to site is via toll road to Sandbanks ferry but take immediate left at mini roundabout before entering toll area and go along gravel roadway; from Sandbanks, pay ferry toll then turn right at mini roundabout and go along gravel road: site is at entrance to Poole Harbour adjacent the Sandbanks/Swanage ferry
Waters accessed:	Poole Harbour and Bay

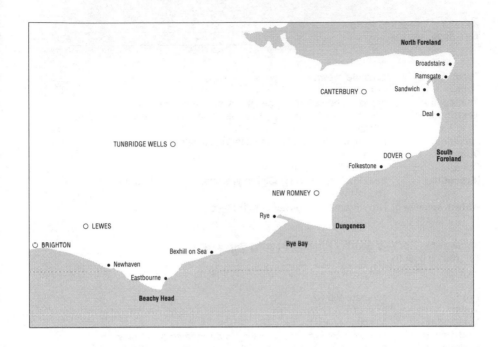

Wareham - Ridge Wharf Yacht Centre
Tel: (0929) 552650

Type:	steep concrete slipway with large winch
Suits:	all craft: river is narrow for sailing dinghies
Availability:	all states of tide except 1 hour either side LW
Restrictions:	4 knot speed limit in river, 10 knots in harbour: water-skiing and jet skis prohibited
Facilities:	fuel on site, parking for car and trailer on site, toilets, chandlery and outboard repairs on site
Dues:	included in launching fee
Charge:	approx. £6 incl parking
Directions:	follow A351 Swanage road, turning left at roundabout at end of Wareham bypass: after 300 yds turn right into new road and yard is ½ mile ahead

Waters accessed: River Frome, Poole Harbour and Bay

Wareham - Redcliffe Farm
Tel: (0929) 552225

Type:	concrete slipway
Suits:	all craft
Availability:	approx. 5 hours either side HW by prior arrangement
Restrictions:	4 knot speed limit in river, 10 knots in harbour: water-skiing and jet skis prohibited
Facilities:	no fuel, parking for car and trailer and toilets on site
Dues:	none
Charge:	approx. £5 inc parking
Directions:	from Poole follow A35/A351 to Wareham, turn off in Stoborough and follow signs
Waters accessed:	River Frome, Poole Harbour (1½ miles)

Hamworthy, Rockley Sands - Rockley Boating Services
Tel: (0202) 665001

Type:	concrete slipway
Suits:	all craft
Availability:	all states of tide
Restrictions:	10 knot speed limit: water-skiing in designated areas only
Facilities:	fuel nearby, parking for car and trailer, toilets, chandlery on site
Dues:	approx. £1.50 (only for craft with engine over 4 hp)
Charge:	approx. £10.50 inc parking
Directions:	from Poole follow A350 to Hamworthy, turning off and following signs to Rockley Point
Waters accessed:	Poole Harbour and Bay

Hamworthy, Lake Drive - Dorset Lake Shipyard (Dorset Yacht Co)
Tel: (0202) 674531/3

Type:	concrete slipway
Suits:	all craft up to 20' LOA
Availability:	all states of tide except 1 hour either side LWS during working hours by prior arrangement
Restrictions:	10 knot speed limit: water-skiing in designated area nearby; no casual launching
Facilities:	fuel, limited parking for car and trailer, crane, toilets, chandlery and other boatyard facilities
Dues:	approx. £1.50 (only for craft with engine over 4 hp)
Charge:	yes: seasonal pass only (£152 for 6 months)
Directions:	from Poole follow A350 to Hamworthy, turning right into Lake Rd and then into Lake Drive: larger boats can take route via Ashmore Ave, Lulworth Ave and thence Lake Drive
Waters accessed:	Poole Harbour and Bay

Hamworthy, Cobbs Quay - Cobbs Quay Ltd, Woodlands Avenue
Tel: (0202) 674299

Type:	two concrete slipways
Suits:	all craft
Availability:	approx. 3 hours either side HW by prior arrangement
Restrictions:	6 knot speed limit: water-skiing in designated areas only
Facilities:	fuel, parking for car and trailer (c), toilets, chandlery, outboard repairs, showers, clubhouse etc all on site
Dues:	approx. £1.50 (only for craft with engine over 4 hp)
Charge:	approx. £5.88
Directions:	from Poole follow A350 to Hamworthy, turn left by Co-op into Hinchcliffe Rd, and follow signs to Cobbs Quay
Waters accessed:	Poole Harbour above Poole Bridge (Bridge opens every 2-3 hours, check with Harbour Office for opening times)

Hamworthy, Cobbs Quay - Davis's Boatyard
Tel: (0202) 674349

Type:	concrete slipway
Suits:	all craft
Availability:	all states of tide except LWS by prior arrangement
Restrictions:	10 knot speed limit: water-skiing in designated area nearby
Facilities:	fuel, parking for car and trailer (c), toilets, and outboard repairs on site, chandlery nearby
Dues:	approx. £1.50 (only for craft with engine over 4 hp)
Charge:	approx. £11.75 (£80 for season)
Directions:	from Poole follow A350 to Hamworthy, turn left by Co-op into Hinchcliffe Rd, then into Woodlands Ave and Cobbs Quay
Waters accessed:	Poole Harbour above Poole Bridge (Bridge opens every 2-3 hours, check with Harbour Office for opening times)

Poole - Baiter Public Slipway
Tel: (0202) 675151 (Poole Borough Council)

Type:	wide concrete slipway
Suits:	all craft
Availability:	all states of tide except LWS
Restrictions:	speed limit: water-skiing in designated area nearby: car park closes at midnight; site can be very busy
Facilities:	fuel nearby, parking for car and trailer and toilets on site; chandlery and outboard repairs nearby
Dues:	approx. £1.50 (only for craft with engine over 4 hp)
Charge:	approx. £5 inc parking
Directions:	from Town Quay follow signs: access is via Newfoundland Drive
Waters accessed:	Poole Harbour and Bay

Sandbanks - Mitchells Boatyard, Turks Lane
Tel: (0202) 747857

Type:	concrete slipway
Suits:	all craft up to 21' LOA
Availability:	approx. 4 hours either side HW by prior arrangement
Restrictions:	10 knot speed limit: water-skiing in designated area nearby; site is very busy in mid-season
Facilities:	fuel($\frac{1}{2}$ mile), parking for car and trailer, toilets, chandlery, outboard repairs all on site
Dues:	approx. £1.50 (only for craft with engine over 4 hp)
Charge:	approx. £10 inc parking
Directions:	from Poole town centre follow Sandbanks Rd, turning into Turks Lane after passing Whitecliff recreation ground
Waters accessed:	Poole Harbour and Bay

Lilliput - Salterns Boatyard, 38 Salterns Way
Tel: (0202) 707321

Type:	concrete slipway, boat hoist and travel hoist
Suits:	all craft
Availability:	all states of tide during working hours by prior arrangement
Restrictions:	10 knot speed limit: water-skiing in designated area nearby
Facilities:	fuel, parking for car and trailer(c), toilets, chandlery, outboard repairs and boatyard facilities all on site; diving supplies nearby
Dues:	approx. £1.50 (only for craft with engine over 4 hp)
Charge:	approx. £15
Directions:	from Poole town centre follow Sandbanks Rd, turning into Salterns Way
Waters accessed:	Poole Harbour and Bay

Sandbanks - Lilliput Yacht Station, 324 Sandbanks Road
Tel: (0202) 707176

Type:	concrete slipway
Suits:	all craft up to 28' LOA
Availability:	approx. 3 hours either side HW during working hours
Restrictions:	10 knot speed limit: water-skiing in designated area nearby; use of site by prior arrangement only
Facilities:	fuel and parking nearby (c), toilets, showers, outboard repairs, moorings
Dues:	approx. £1.50 (only for craft with engine over 4 hp)
Charge:	approx. £10
Directions:	from Poole town centre follow Sandbanks Rd
Waters accessed:	Poole Harbour and Bay

Sandbanks - Sandbanks Yacht Co Ltd, 32 Panorama Road
Tel: (0202) 707500

Type:	concrete slipway
Suits:	all craft up to 22' LOA
Availability:	all states of tide except within 1-2 hours LWS
Restrictions:	10 knot speed limit: water-skiing permitted in designated areas
Facilities:	fuel on site, parking for car and trailer on site, toilets, chandlery, moorings, repairs and boat storage all available on site
Dues:	approx. £1.50 (only for craft with engine over 4 hp)
Charge:	approx. £10 inc. parking
Directions:	from Poole town centre follow signs to Sandbanks, Panorama Rd is near Sandbanks ferry terminal
Waters accessed:	Poole Harbour and Bay

Southbourne - Wick Lane

Type:	concrete slipway
Suits:	dinghies and small powered craft
Availability:	approx. 2½ hours either side double HW
Restrictions:	4 knot speed limit: water-skiing and jet skis prohibited; currents in harbour entrance are strong
Facilities:	fuel nearby, limited parking for car and trailer (c), toilets on site
Dues:	none
Charge:	none
Directions:	from Bournemouth follow B3059, turning right into Wick Lane before Tuckton Bridge: site is on south bank downstream of bridge
Waters accessed:	River Stour, Christchurch Harbour and Bay

Christchurch - Quomps, Mayors Mead Car Park
Tel: (0202) 486321 ext. 260 (Quay and Moorings Superintendent)

Type:	wide concrete slipway
Suits:	all craft except pwc
Availability:	all states of tide except within 1 hour LW
Restrictions:	4 knot speed limit in harbour: water-skiing and jet skis prohibited
Facilities:	fuel nearby, parking for car and trailer on site (c), toilets on site, other facilities available nearby
Dues:	none
Charge:	none
Directions:	from Bournemouth follow B3059 towards Christchurch, turning right at roundabout after Tuckton Bridge into Willow Drive: site is adjacent Wick Ferry Holiday Centre (Pontins) and approach is through car park
Waters accessed:	River Stour, Christchurch Harbour and Bay

Christchurch - Rossiter Yachts Ltd. Bridge Street
Tel: (0202) 483250

Type:	concrete slipway
Suits:	all craft except pwc
Availability:	1 hour either side double HW from 0800 -1700 mon-sat by prior arrangement only
Restrictions:	4 knot speed limit in harbour: water-skiing and jet skis prohibited
Facilities:	diesel on site, petrol nearby, parking for car and trailer on site, toilets nearby, chandlery and short stay alongside berths available
Dues:	none
Charge:	approx. £30
Directions:	follow signs to town centre; at roundabout turn into High St and follow until road becomes Bridge St: access is between two bridges
Waters accessed:	River Avon leading to Christchurch Harbour and Bay

Christchurch - Bridge Street
Tel: (0202) 486321 ext. 260 (Quay and Moorings Superintendent)

Type:	concrete slipway
Suits:	small powered craft and sailing dinghies only
Availability:	approx. 1 hour either side double HW
Restrictions:	4 knot speed limit in harbour: water-skiing and jet skis prohibited
Facilities:	fuel nearby, parking for car and trailer on site (c), toilets on site
Dues:	none
Charge:	none
Directions:	follow B3059 to town centre turning right into Barrack Rd (A35); at roundabout turn into High St and follow into Bridge St: site is on east bank of river adjacent car park in front of Civic Offices
Waters accessed:	River Avon leading into Christchurch Harbour and Bay

Christchurch - Fisherman's Bank, Argyle Road
Tel: (0202) 486321 ext. 260 (Quay and Moorings Superintendent)

Type:	tarmac and shingle foreshore
Suits:	small powered craft and sailing dinghies only
Availability:	approx. 1 hour either side double HW
Restrictions:	4 knot speed limit in harbour: water-skiing and jet skis prohibited; turning and manoeuvring space is very restricted as Argyle Rd is a narrow cul-de-sac
Facilities:	fuel from Stanpit Garage nearby, limited parking in nearby streets, toilets, chandlers and other facilities available nearby
Dues:	none
Charge:	none
Directions:	from town centre follow B3059 east turn off following signs to Stanpit turning into Argyle Rd after passing garage
Waters accessed:	Christchurch Harbour and Bay

Mudeford Quay

Tel: (0202) 486321 ext. 260 (Quay and Moorings Superintendent)

Type:	concrete slipway onto hard foreshore
Suits:	all craft except jet skis
Availability:	approx. 1 hour either side double HW
Restrictions:	4 knot speed limit in harbour: water-skiing and jet skis prohibited
Facilities:	fuel from garage (2 miles), parking for car and trailer on site (c), toilets on site, other facilities nearby
Dues:	none
Charge:	approx. £2.50 (hand-launched craft) and £4 (vehicle-launched craft) on summer weekends only
Directions:	from town centre follow B3059 east turn off following signs to Mudeford: access is through car park on Quay
Waters accessed:	Christchurch Harbour and Bay

Keyhaven - The Quay Slipway

Tel: (0590) 645695

Type:	concrete slipway onto shingle
Suits:	all craft up to 20' LOA
Availability:	approx. 3 hours either side HW
Restrictions:	6 knot speed limit in river and within 300m of shore: water-skiing prohibited
Facilities:	fuel in Milford, parking for car and trailer (c) and toilets on site
Dues:	none
Charge:	none
Directions:	from Lymington or New Milton take A337 following signs to Milford-on-Sea and Keyhaven: after passing Gun Inn turn left towards Keyhaven YC and entrance to Quay will be seen ahead
Waters accessed:	Keyhaven Lake and Western Solent

Lymington - Harbour Commissioner's Slip, Town Quay

Tel: (0590) 672014

Type:	concrete slipway onto gravel
Suits:	all craft
Availability:	all states of tide
Restrictions:	6 knot speed limit in river: water-skiing and windsurfing prohibited
Facilities:	fuel nearby, parking for car and trailer (c) and toilets on site; chandlery and outboard repairs nearby
Dues:	none
Charge:	approx. £3.50 (annual season - £50)
Directions:	leave M27 at junction 1 and taking A337 to town centre: site is at far end of car park on Town Quay
Waters accessed:	Lymington River and Western Solent

Lymington - Harbour Commissioner's Slip, Bath Road
Tel: (0590) 672014

Type:	concrete slipway onto gravel
Suits:	all craft
Availability:	all states of tide except 1 hour either side LWS
Restrictions:	6 knot speed limit in river: water-skiing and windsurfing prohibited; take care when ferries approaching
Facilities:	fuel nearby, parking for car and trailer (c) and toilets on site; chandlery and outboard repairs nearby
Dues:	none
Charge:	approx. £3.50 (annual season - £50)
Directions:	leave M27 at junction 1 taking A337 to town centre and turn right at bottom of High St: site is past Lymington Marina
Waters accessed:	Lymington River and Western Solent

Beaulieu River - Bucklers Hard Yacht Harbour
Tel: (0590) 616200/616234 (Harbour Master)

Type:	concrete slipway
Suits:	all craft except jet skis
Availability:	approx. 5 hours either side HW
Restrictions:	5 knot speed limit: water-skiing and jet skis prohibited
Facilities:	fuel, parking for car and trailer, toilets and chandlery, outboard repairs, shop, hotel and maritime museum all on site
Dues:	approx. £7 inc parking for car and trailer
Charge:	no additional fee
Directions:	leave M27 at junction 1 and take A337 to Lyndhurst then B3056 to Beaulieu following signs to Bucklers Hard; take the third turning left just before Bucklers Hard village
Waters accessed:	Beaulieu River and The Solent

Yarmouth - South Quay
Tel: (0983) 760321 (Harbour Office)

Type:	two concrete slipways into harbour
Suits:	all craft
Availability:	all states of tide by prior arrangement
Restrictions:	4 knot speed limit in harbour: water-skiing permitted in designated areas; keep clear of ferries entering and leaving the harbour at all times
Facilities:	fuel, parking for car and trailer (c) and toilets on site, other facilities nearby
Dues:	none
Charge:	none
Directions:	from Cowes follow A3020 and A3054 west or ferry fom Lymington
Waters accessed:	Western Solent

Gurnard - Shore Road

Type:	concrete slipway
Suits:	small craft and windsurfers only
Availability:	approx. 3 hours either side HW
Restrictions:	10 knot speed limit within 2 miles of Solent beaches
Facilities:	no fuel, limited parking, trailers can be left by slip, toilets
Dues:	none known
Charge:	none
Directions:	from Cowes take A3020 or B3325 and follow signs to Gurnard: site is adjacent sailing club
Waters accessed:	Western Solent

West Cowes - Egypt Point Slip
Tel: (0983) 293952 (Harbour Office, Town Quay)

Type:	concrete slipway
Suits:	all craft
Availability:	approx 3 hours either side HW
Restrictions:	6 knot speed limit in harbour: board sailers must keep clear of the main channel; jet skiers must keep in the channel
Facilities:	no fuel, parking for car and trailer (c), toilets, chandlers
Dues:	none
Charge:	none
Directions:	site is at junction of Egypt Hill and the Esplanade
Waters accessed:	River Medina, Cowes Harbour and The Solent

West Cowes - Watch House Slip, Parade
Tel: (0983) 293952 (Harbour Office, Town Quay)

Type:	concrete slipway
Suits:	small powered craft and sailing dinghies
Availability:	approx. 4 hours either side HW
Restrictions:	6 knot speed limit in harbour: board sailers must keep clear of the main channel; jet skiers must keep in the channel; site may be congested at peak times
Facilities:	fuel nearby, parking for car and trailer nearby (c)
Dues:	none
Charge:	none
Directions:	access is from the southern end of the Parade
Waters accessed:	River Medina, Cowes Harbour and The Solent

West Cowes - Sun Hill Slip, High Street
Tel: (0983) 293952 (Harbour Office, Town Quay)

Type:	concrete and stone slipway onto shingle
Suits:	sailing dinghies only
Availability:	approx. 3 hours either side HW: key available 0900 - 1700 from Midland Bank or Harbour Office
Restrictions:	6 knot speed limit in harbour: board-sailers must keep clear of main channel; jet skiers must keep within channel; access is via narrow pedestrianised road with a locked barrier
Facilities:	fuel nearby, parking for car and trailer nearby (c), most other facilities available in town
Dues:	none
Charge:	none
Directions:	site is off High St, adjacent Midland Bank and opposite Sun Hill
Waters accessed:	River Medina, Cowes Harbour and the Solent

West Cowes - Town Quay Slip, High Street
Tel: (0983) 293952 (Harbour Office, Town Quay)

Type:	concrete slipway onto mud
Suits:	sailing dinghies only
Availability:	approx. 4 hours either side HW
Restrictions:	6 knot speed limit in harbour: board sailers must keep clear of main channel; jet skiers must keep within channel; entrance to site is obstructed by portable posts and chains
Facilities:	fuel nearby, parking for car and trailer nearby (c), most other facilities available in town
Dues:	none
Charge:	none
Directions:	site is adjacent the Fountain Hotel and the Red Funnel Ferry Terminal in the High St; access is via the one-way system
Waters accessed:	River Medina, Cowes Harbour and the Solent

West Cowes - Thetis Wharf, Medina Road
Tel: (0983) 293952 (Harbour Office, Town Quay)

Type:	concrete slipway onto shingle
Suits:	sailing dinghies only
Availability:	approx. 4 hours either side HW
Restrictions:	6 knot speed limit in harbour: board sailers must keep clear of main channel; jet skiers must keep within the channel
Facilities:	fuel nearby, parking for car and trailer nearby (c), most other facilities available in town
Dues:	none
Charge:	none
Directions:	from town centre, follow directions to Floating Bridge: site is opposite Bridge Rd at northern end of Medina Rd
Waters accessed:	River Medina, Cowes Harbour and the Solent

East Cowes - White Hart Slip, Dover Road
Tel: (0983) 293952 (Harbour Office, Town Quay)

Type:	narrow concrete slipway
Suits:	sailing dinghies only
Availability:	approx. 4 hours either side HW
Restrictions:	6 knot speed limit in harbour: board sailers must keep clear of main channel; jet skiers must keep in channel
Facilities:	fuel nearby, parking for car and trailer nearby (c), most other facilities available in town
Dues:	none
Charge:	none
Directions:	site is adjacent Red Funnel Ferry Terminal and vehicular access is restricted
Waters accessed:	River Medina, Cowes Harbour and the Solent

East Cowes - Albany Road
Tel: (0983) 293952 (Harbour Office, Town Quay)

Type:	short, stepped masonry slipway
Suits:	small craft which can be manhandled only
Availability:	HW only
Restrictions:	6 knot speed limit in harbour: board sailers must keep clear of main channel; jet skiers must keep in channel
Facilities:	no fuel, parking for car and trailer, toilets
Dues:	none
Charge:	none
Directions:	access is via the Esplanade
Waters accessed:	River Medina, Cowes Harbour and the Solent

Newport - Town Quay
Tel: (0983) 525994

Type:	steep cobbled slipway
Suits:	all craft up to 20' LOA
Availability:	approx. 1½ hours either side HW
Restrictions:	4 knot speed limit: site is on corner of busy road with no pavement; Seaclose Quay is a better site
Facilities:	fuel, parking for car only, hand operated crane, toilets in summer only, chandlery and repairs nearby
Dues:	none
Charge:	none
Directions:	from Cowes follow A3020 or from Ryde the A3054: site is at the junction of Sea St with the Town Quay
Waters accessed:	River Medina and the Solent

Newport - Seaclose Quay
Tel: (0983) 525994

Type:	concrete slipway
Suits:	all craft up to 20' LOA
Availability:	approx. 1½ hours either side HW
Restrictions:	4 knot speed limit: care needed`as site is close to entrance of large transport yard which must not be obstructed
Facilities:	no fuel, no parking, toilets in summer only, chandlery and repairs nearby; this is the best site in Newport
Dues:	none
Charge:	none
Directions:	from Cowes follow A3020 or from Ryde the A3054: site is reached via the Town Quay
Waters accessed:	River Medina, Cowes Harbour and the Solent

Newport - Island Harbour Marina, Mill Lane
Tel: (0983) 526020

Type:	concrete slipway into locked basin
Suits:	all craft up to 50' LOA
Availability:	approx. 4 hours either side HW by prior arrangement
Restrictions:	speed limit in harbour
Facilities:	diesel on site, petrol nearby, parking for car and trailer, toilets, showers (c), engine repairs, launderette, boatbulding, overnight berths, pub and restaurant facilities
Dues:	none
Charge:	approx. £21
Directions:	from Newport or Ryde follow A3054 turning off into Fairlee Rd: site is on east bank of river downstream of Newport
Waters accessed:	River Medina, Cowes Harbour and the Solent

Whippingham - The Folly

Type:	concrete slipway
Suits:	all craft
Availability:	all states of tide
Restrictions:	6 knot speed limit in Folly Reach
Facilities:	fuel nearby, parking for car and trailer (c), toilets and showers, pub and restaurant facilities in pub
Dues:	none
Charge:	none
Directions:	from Newport or Ryde follow A3054 turning off into Folly Lane: site is on east bank of river, upstream of East Cowes and access is through The Folly Inn car park
Waters accessed:	River Medina, Cowes Harbour and The Solent

Ryde - St Thomas' Street
Tel: (0983) 613879 (Harbour Master)

Type:	concrete slipway onto beach
Suits:	small craft only
Availability:	approx. 3 hours either side HW
Restrictions:	6 knot speed limit inshore
Facilities:	no fuel, parking for car only (c), toilets
Dues:	none
Charge:	none
Directions:	site is to the west of pier
Waters accessed:	The Solent

Ryde - Harbour Slipway
Tel (0983) 613879 (Harbour Master)

Type:	concrete slipway
Suits:	small craft only
Availability:	approx. 3 hours either side HW
Restrictions:	6 knot speed limit inshore
Facilities:	parking for car and trailer (c), toilets
Dues:	none
Charge:	none
Directions:	site is east of pier and access is from the Esplanade
Waters accessed:	The Solent

Ryde - Cornwall Street
Tel (0983) 613879 (Harbour Master)

Type:	sand covered cobbled slipway
Suits:	small craft only
Availability:	near HW only
Restrictions:	6 knot speed limit inshore
Facilities:	parking for car and trailer nearby (c)
Dues:	none
Charge:	none
Directions:	site is near the harbour
Waters accessed:	The Solent

Ryde - Northwalk
Tel: (0983) 613879 (Harbour Master)

Type:	iron slipway onto beach
Suits:	small craft only
Availability:	approx. 3 hours either side HW
Restrictions:	6 knot speed limit inshore
Facilities:	no fuel, parking for car and trailer (c), no toilets

Dues:	none
Charge:	none
Directions:	site is to the east of pier and opposite the canoe lake
Waters accessed:	The Solent

Ryde - Appley Slip, Northwalk
Tel: (0983) 613879 (Harbour Master)

Type:	concrete slipway onto beach
Suits:	small craft only
Availability:	approx. 3 hours either side HW
Restrictions:	6 knot speed limit inshore
Facilities:	no fuel, parking for car and trailer (c), toilets
Dues:	none
Charge:	none
Directions:	site is at the east end of Northwalk at Appley Park by the Tower Boathouse: Ryde Rescue operate from this site
Waters accessed:	The Solent

Seaview - Springvale Slip

Type:	concrete slipway onto beach
Suits:	small craft only
Availability:	approx. 3 hours either side HW
Restrictions:	6 knot speed limit inshore
Facilities:	no fuel, no parking, toilets
Dues:	none
Charge:	none
Directions:	from Ryde follow B3330 and signs to Seaview: site is opposite Battery Hotel and access is via Springvale Rd
Waters accessed:	The Solent

Seaview - Esplanade

Type:	very steep concrete slipway with sharp bend onto shingle
Suits:	small craft only
Availability:	approx. 3 hours either side HW
Restrictions:	6 knot speed limit inshore
Facilities:	no fuel, no parking, no toilets
Dues:	none
Charge:	none
Directions:	from Ryde follow B3330 and signs to Seaview and seafront: site is at junction of High St and Esplanade on sharp bend
Waters accessed:	The Solent

Seagrove Bay

Type:	concrete slipway
Suits:	small craft only
Availability:	approx. 3 hours either side HW
Restrictions:	6 knot speed limit inshore
Facilities:	no fuel or parking, toilets
Dues:	none
Charge:	none
Directions:	from Ryde follow B3330: site is at southern end of bay and access is via Gully Rd
Waters accessed:	The Solent

St Helens Duver

Type:	concrete slipway
Suits:	all craft
Availability:	approx. 3 hours either side HW
Restrictions:	6 knot speed limit inshore
Facilities:	no fuel, parking for car and trailer (c), toilets, cafe
Dues:	none
Charge:	yes
Directions:	from Ryde follow B3330 to St Helens and signs to The Duver: access is through car park (c)
Waters accessed:	The Solent

The Duver, St Helens - H Attrill & Sons (IOW) Ltd
Tel: (0983) 872319

Type:	concrete slipway
Suits:	all craft: craft over 20' LOA launched by yard staff only
Availability:	approx. 3 hours either side HW
Restrictions:	speed limit in harbour: jet skis prohibited; tides in harbour entrance run very strongly
Facilities:	diesel, parking for car and trailer (c)
Dues:	none
Charge:	approx £19 for craft under 20' LOA
Directions:	from Ryde follow B3330 to St Helens then private road across The Duver
Waters accessed:	Bembridge Harbour and The Solent

Bembridge Harbour - Bembridge Outboards, Embankment Road
Tel: (0983) 872817

Type:	concrete slipway
Suits:	all craft except jet skis

Availability:	approx. 2½ hours either side HW; contact owners to ensure site will not be obstructed
Restrictions:	10 knot speed limit within 2 miles of any Solent beach; no jet skis allowed in harbour; tide in harbour entrance runs very strongly
Facilities:	diesel nearby, petrol (2 miles), parking for car and trailer nearby, toilets available during working hours, outboard repairs on site, chandlers nearby
Dues:	none
Charge:	approx. £2
Directions:	take A3055 and B3330 from Ryde: access is via Embankment Rd on south shore of harbour
Waters accessed:	Bembridge Harbour and the Solent

Bembridge Harbour - A.A.Coombes, Embankment Road
Tel: (0983) 872296

Type:	concrete slipway
Suits:	all craft except jet skis
Availability:	approx. 2 hours either side HW: contact yard to ensure site will be available
Restrictions:	10 knot speed limit within 2 mile of all Solent beaches: no jet skis allowed in harbour; tides in harbour entrance run very strongly
Facilities:	diesel on site, petrol 2 miles, parking for car and trailer 200 yds (c), toilets nearby, chandlery, boat repairs, storage, moorings all available on site; outboard repairs from Bembridge Outboards adjacent
Dues:	none
Charge:	approx. £2
Directions:	take A3055 and B3330 from Ryde: site is on Embankment Rd which runs around harbour from St Helens to Bembridge village
Waters accessed:	Bembridge Harbour and the Solent

Calshot Spit - Calshot Activities Centre
Tel: (0703) 892077

Type:	wide concrete slipway
Suits:	all craft: assisted launch available by prior arrangement
Availability:	at all states of tide from 0830 - 2200
Restrictions:	10 knot speed limit within 2 miles of all Solent beaches: do not obstruct dinghy sailers under tuition; site is very close to main shipping channel and all craft must have 3rd party insurance
Facilities:	fuel (12 miles), parking for car and trailer on site, toilets and showers, bar and cafe, boat park, storage for craft up to 40' LOA and accommodation all available on site
Dues:	none
Charge:	approx. £5 inc parking and use of facilties
Directions:	from Southampton take the A326 to Fawley then B3053 to Calshot Spit and Castle
Waters accessed:	Southampton Water and The Solent

Fawley - Ashlett Creek

Type:	shingle hard
Suits:	sailing dinghies and trailer-sailers
Availability:	approx. 3 hours either side HW
Restrictions:	6 knot speed limit: no water-skiing or jet skis; narrow access road
Facilities:	no fuel, limited parking for car and trailer on site, toilets nearby, pub
Dues:	none
Charge:	none
Directions:	from Southampton take the A326 to Fawley then B3053 and turn off to Ashlett
Waters accessed:	Southampton Water and The Solent

Hythe - Hythe Marina Village
Tel: (0703) 849263 (Lock Control)

Type:	concrete slipway
Suits:	all craft
Availability:	approx. 4 hours either side HW
Restrictions:	6 knot speed limit: no water-skiing or jet skis
Facilities:	fuel, parking for car and trailer, toilets, showers, telephone, chandlery and all marina facilities are adjacent
Dues:	none
Charge:	none
Directions:	from Southampton follow A326 towards Fawley and follow signs to marina and slipway
Waters accessed:	Southampton Water and The Solent

Marchwood - Cracknore Hard
Tel: (0703) 330022 (Harbour Master)

Type:	rather soft shingle hard
Suits:	small craft which can be manhandled only
Availability:	approx. 4 hours either side HW
Restrictions:	6 knot speed limit: water-skiing prohibited; access is narrow and rough - this is a poor site
Facilities:	no facilities apart from very limited parking
Dues:	none
Charge:	none
Directions:	from Southampton follow the A326, turning left into Marchwood and following signs to hard
Waters accessed:	Southampton Water and The Solent

Marchwood - Magazine Lane
Tel: (0703) 330022

Type:	shingle hard
Suits:	craft up to about 15' LOA
Availability:	approx. 4 hours either side HW
Restrictions:	6 knot speed limit: water-skiing prohibited; access is narrow and rough and turning space very limited
Facilities:	no fuel, parking for car and trailer on site: Marchwood Y.C. adjacent
Dues:	none
Charge:	none
Directions:	follow A326 from Southampton turning left into Marchwood: Magazine Lane is on left before disused power station
Waters accessed:	Southampton Water and The Solent

Eling Creek - Eling Quay
Tel: (0703) 863138

Type:	shingle hard with drop at end onto mud
Suits:	all craft except jet skis
Availability:	approx. 2 hours either side HW
Restrictions:	6 knot speed limit: water-skiing and jet skis prohibited
Facilities:	parking for car and trailer on site, toilets nearby
Dues:	none
Charge:	none
Directions:	from the M27 take the A271 following signs to Eling Tide Mill: site is adjacent Anchor Inn and tide mill
Waters accessed:	Southampton Water and The Solent

Southampton, Chapel - Crosshouse Hard
Tel: (0703) 832204 (Development Officer)

Type:	concrete slipway onto muddy shore
Suits:	small shallow draught craft
Availability:	approx. 5 hours either side HW
Restrictions:	6 knot speed limit: water-skiing prohibited
Facilities:	fuel from garage, parking for car and trailer (not overnight)
Dues:	none
Charge:	none
Directions:	site is on west side of river just north of the Itchen Bridge: access is via Crosshouse Rd
Waters accessed:	River Itchen, Southampton Water and The Solent

Southampton, St Denys - Priory Hard
Tel: (0703) 832204 (Development Officer)

Type:	concrete slipway and gravel hard
Suits:	small shallow draught craft
Availability:	approx. 5 hours either side HW
Restrictions:	6 knot speed limit: no water-skiing
Facilities:	fuel from garage, limited parking for car and trailer
Dues:	none
Charge:	none
Directions:	from city centre follow signs to St Denys Station: site is on west side of river south of the station and access is via Priory Rd

Waters accessed: River Itchen, Southampton Water and The Solent

Southampton, Woolston - Itchen Ferry Hard
Tel: (0703) 832204 (Development Officer)

Type:	concrete slipway and gravel hard
Suits:	small shallow draught craft
Availability:	approx. 5 hours either side HW
Restrictions:	6 knot speed limit: water-skiing prohibited
Facilities:	fuel from garage, parking for car and trailer on street only, no toilets, chandlery nearby
Dues:	none
Charge:	none
Directions:	leave M27 at junction 8 and follow A3025 to Woolston or from city centre cross Itchen Bridge: site is on east side of river just north of the bridge and access is via Hazel Rd

Waters accessed: River Itchen, Southampton Water and The Solent

Southampton, Woolston - Victoria Road Slipway
Tel: (0703) 832204 (Development Officer)

Type:	concrete slipway with central wooden skid
Suits:	small craft and craft with keels up to approx. 20' LOA
Availability:	most states of tide
Restrictions:	6 knot speed limit: water-skiing prohibited
Facilities:	fuel from garage, parking for car and trailer, chandlery nearby
Dues:	none
Charge:	none
Directions:	leave M27 at junction 8 and follow A3025 to Woolston or from city centre cross Itchen Bridge: site is on east side of river south of the bridge and adjacent Southampton S.C. clubhouse, access is via Victoria Rd

Waters accessed: River Itchen, Southampton Water and The Solent

Weston - Weston Shore Slipway, Weston Lane
Tel: (0703) 832204 (Development Officer)

Type:	slipway and gravel hard
Suits:	small craft
Availability:	approx. 2 hours either side HW
Restrictions:	6 knot speed limit: water-skiing permitted in designated areas
Facilities:	no fuel, parking for car and trailer (not overnight), toilets,
Dues:	none
Charge:	none
Directions:	leave M27 at junction 8 and follow A3025 turning off to Weston: site is at end of Weston Lane and access is via Weston Parade
Waters accessed:	Southampton Water and The Solent

Netley Abbey - Beach Lane Slipway

Type:	concrete slipway onto shingle
Suits:	small craft
Availability:	approx. 2 hours either side HW
Restrictions:	6 knot speed limit: water-skiing permitted in designated areas
Facilities:	fuel in village, parking for car and trailer, toilets,
Dues:	none
Charge:	none
Directions:	leave M27 at junction 8 and follow A3025 turning off to Netley Abbey: site is approached via Victoria Rd
Waters accessed:	Southampton Water and The Solent

Netley Abbey - Victoria Road Slipway

Type:	concrete slipway onto soft shingle
Suits:	small craft
Availability:	approx. 2 hours either side HW
Restrictions:	6 knot speed limit: water-skiing permitted in designated areas
Facilities:	fuel in village, parking for car and trailer, toilets,
Dues:	none
Charge:	none
Directions:	leave M27 at junction 8 and follow A3025 turning off to Netley Abbey and following signs to Royal Victoria Country Park: site is outside entrance to park
Waters accessed:	Southampton Water and The Solent

Hamble - Hamble Quay, High Street
Tel: (0489) 576387 (Harbour Office)

Type:	launching over shingle hard
Suits:	all craft up to approx. 24' LOA

Availability:	approx. 4 hours either side HW
Restrictions:	6 knot speed limit: water-skiing prohibited; popular and busy site
Facilities:	fuel in village or at local marinas, limited parking for car and trailer (often congested), toilets, chandlery nearby
Dues:	none
Charge:	none
Directions:	leave M27 at junction 8 and follow B3397 to Hamble: site is at end of High St adjacent Royal Southern YC and opposite the Bugle Inn
Waters accessed:	River Hamble, Southampton Water and The Solent

Hamble - Port Hamble Marina
Tel: (0703) 454111 (Hamble Yacht Services)

Type:	concrete slipway
Suits:	larger craft only
Availability:	all states of tide
Restrictions:	6 knot speed limit: water-skiing prohibited; check for availability
Facilities:	fuel, limited parking for car and trailer, toilets, showers, chandlery and other marina facilities all on site
Dues:	none
Charge:	min charge £59
Directions:	leave M27 at junction 8 and follow B3397 to Hamble and signs
Waters accessed:	River Hamble, Southampton Water and The Solent

Hamble - Mercury Yacht Harbour
Tel: (0703) 455994

Type:	concrete slipway
Suits:	all craft
Availability:	all states of tide except 1 hour either side LWS
Restrictions:	6 knot speed limit: water-skiing prohibited; check for availability
Facilities:	parking for car and trailer (c), toilets, showers, chandlery and other marina facilities
Dues:	none
Charge:	approx. £11.75
Directions:	leave M27 at junction 8 and follow B3397 to Hamble and signs
Waters accessed:	River Hamble, Southampton Water and The Solent

Bursledon - Lands End Road
Tel: (0489) 576387 (Harbour Office)

Type:	shingle foreshore
Suits:	dinghies only
Availability:	approx. 4-5 hours either side HW
Restrictions:	6 knot speed limit: water-skiing prohibited in river
Facilities:	fuel nearby, parking at station (½ mile), pub, chandlery nearby
Dues:	none

Charge:	none
Directions:	leave M27 at junction 8 and follow A27 to Bursledon, turning right in village towards Bursledon Pt: site is opposite Moody's Boatyard and close to "Jolly Sailor" pub
Waters accessed:	River Hamble, Southampton Water and The Solent

Lower Swanwick - Swanwick Shore Road
Tel: (0489) 576387 (Harbour Office)

Type:	shingle hard
Suits:	small craft
Availability:	approx. 4-5 hours either side HW
Restrictions:	6 knot speed limit: water-skiing prohibited in river
Facilities:	fuel nearby, limited parking nearby, chandlery nearby in marina
Dues:	none
Charge:	none
Directions:	leave M27 at junction 9 and follow A27: site is just downstream of Moody's Boatyard
Waters accessed:	River Hamble, Southampton Water and The Solent

Warsash - Shore Road Hard
Tel: (0489) 576387 (Harbour Office)

Type:	shingle hard
Suits:	all craft
Availability:	all states of tide
Restrictions:	6 knot speed limit: water-skiing prohibited in river
Facilities:	fuel nearby, limited parking nearby, toilets, chandlery nearby
Dues:	none
Charge:	none
Directions:	leave A27 at Park Gate via Brook Lane following signs for Warsash and turning right along Shore Rd: site is on east bank of river near mouth opposite "The Rising Sun"
Waters accessed:	River Hamble, Southampton Water and The Solent

Hill Head - site adjacent Hill Head S.C.
Tel: (0329) 236100 extn.2547 (Fareham B.C. Leisure Unit)

Type:	concrete slipway
Suits:	sailing dinghies and small powered craft
Availability:	approx. 2 hours either side HW
Restrictions:	speed limit inshore
Facilities:	parking for car and trailer, Hill Head S.C. adjacent
Dues:	none
Charge:	none
Directions:	follow A27 west of Fareham and signs to Hill Head
Waters accessed:	The Solent

Hill Head - Salterns Road
Tel: (0329) 236100 extn.2547 (Fareham B.C. Leisure Unit)

Type:	timber ramp onto shingle beach
Suits:	sailing dinghies and small powercraft
Availability:	approx. 2 hours either side HW
Restrictions:	speed limit inshore: popular and busy site
Facilities:	parking, toilets, Salterns S.C. adjacent
Dues:	none
Charge:	none
Directions:	turn off the A27 west of Fareham following signs to Hill Head: site is at end of large car park
Waters accessed:	The Solent

Lee-on-Solent - Marine Parade East

Type:	steep concrete slipway
Suits:	all craft
Availability:	approx. 4 hours either side HW
Restrictions:	7 knot speed limit within 1km of beach: water-skiing permitted in designated area
Facilities:	no fuel, parking for car and trailer (c), toilets, chandlery nearby
Dues:	none
Charge:	none
Directions:	leave M27 at junction11 following A27 then B3385 to seafront
Waters accessed:	The Solent

Lee-on-Solent - Solent Gardens

Type:	concrete slipway onto shingle
Suits:	all craft
Availability:	approx. 2½ hours either side HW or over shingle at all times
Restrictions:	7 knot speed limit within 1km of beach: water-skiing permitted in designated area
Facilities:	no fuel, parking for car and trailer (c), toilets, chandlery from Gosport
Dues:	none
Charge:	none
Directions:	leave M27 at junction11 following A27 then B3385 to seafront
Waters accessed:	The Solent

Type:	3 concrete slipways: best one is at No 2 battery
Suits:	all craft
Availability:	approx. 4 hours either side HW or over shingle at all times
Restrictions:	10 knot speed limit within ½ mile of shore: water-skiing permitted in designated area off Lee-on-Solent
Facilities:	no fuel, parking for car and trailer (c), toilets, chandlery from Gosport
Dues:	none
Charge:	none
Directions:	leave M27 at junction11 and follow A27 then B3385/B3333 to seafront
Waters accessed:	The Solent

Gosport - Hardway

Type:	steep concrete slipway
Suits:	all craft
Availability:	approx. 4½ hours either side HW
Restrictions:	10 knot speed limit: water-skiing prohibited
Facilities:	diesel, parking for car and trailer, toilets in car park, chandlery nearby
Dues:	none
Charge:	none
Directions:	leave M27 at junction11 and take A27/A32 Gosport Rd and follow signs: site is adjacent 105 Priory Rd
Waters accessed:	Portsmouth Harbour and The Solent

Fareham - Lower Quay
Tel: (0829) 236100 ext. 2547 (Leisure Unit)

Type:	concrete slipway
Suits:	all craft
Availability:	approx. 2 hours either side HW
Restrictions:	10 knot speed limit: water-skiing prohibited
Facilities:	diesel nearby, parking for car and trailer, toilets nearby, chandlery nearby
Dues:	none
Charge:	none
Directions:	leave M27 at junction11 and follow A27: site is adjacent Lower Quay
Waters accessed:	Portsmouth Harbour and The Solent

Paulsgrove

Type:	concrete slipway
Suits:	all craft
Availability:	approx. 2½ hours either side HW
Restrictions:	10 knot speed limit: water-skiing prohibited
Facilities:	no fuel, limited parking, no toilets, chandlers in Fareham
Dues:	none
Charge:	none
Directions:	leave M27 at junction11 and follow A27 east, turn off at signpost to 'Royal Navy Firefighting School'
Waters accessed:	Portsmouth Harbour and The Solent

Portsmouth - Port Solent
Tel: (0705) 210765

Type:	launching by crane or boat hoist only
Suits:	all craft
Availability:	0800-1800 daily by prior arrangement only
Restrictions:	10 knot speed limit: water-skiing prohibited
Facilities:	fuel, parking for car and trailer, toilets, chandlery, outboard repairs, shops and restaurants all on site
Dues:	none
Charge:	approx. £36.50
Directions:	from the west, leave the M27 at junction 12; from the east, take the Hilsea exit and follow signs to Port Solent
Waters accessed:	Portsmouth Harbour and The Solent

Portsmouth - Camber Quay, East Street
Tel: (0705) 297391 ext. 310 (Berthing Master)

Type:	wide concrete slipway
Suits:	all craft except jet skis
Availability:	0800 -1600 daily by arrangement with Berthing Master
Restrictions:	10 knot speed limit in harbour: jet skis prohibited; locked barrier - key from Berthing Master; watch out for Isle of Wight ferries using berthing facilities opposite slipway
Facilities:	fuel nearby, parking for car and trailer, toilets and chandlery on site, other facilities available nearby
Dues:	none but licence required
Charge:	approx. £2
Directions:	follow signs to Old Portsmouth from M27/M275: site is old Isle of Wight ferry slip
Waters accessed:	Porstmouth Harbour and The Solent

Eastney Beach
Tel: (0705) 463419 (Harbour Office)

Type:	concrete slipway often covered by sand and shingle
Suits:	all craft; beware strong tidal currents, especially on spring tides
Availability:	all states of tide
Restrictions:	10 knot speed limit in harbour: water-skiing permitted in designated area under licence only; jet skis require a transit permit;
Facilities:	no fuel, parking for car and trailer and toilets nearby
Dues:	approx. £4.65 (annual fee £19)
Charge:	no additional fee
Directions:	from M27/A27 folow A2030 and signs to Southsea, turning off to follow signs to Langstone Marina and Fort Cumberland: site is just south of Eastney CA clubhouse
Waters accessed:	Langstone Harbour and The Solent

Havant - Brockhampton Quay
Tel: (0705) 463419 (Harbour Office)

Type:	wide concrete slipway
Suits:	all craft
Availability:	approx. 1½ hours either side HW
Restrictions:	10 knot speed limit in harbour: water skiing permitted in designated area only under licence; jet skis require transit permit; access has height restriction
Facilities:	no fuel, parking for car and trailer on site
Dues:	approx. £4.65 (annual fee £19)
Charge:	no additional fee
Directions:	fom A27 follow signs to the Public Amenity Tip and site is adjacent
Waters accessed:	Langstone Harbour and The Solent

Hayling Island - Ferry Point
Tel: (0705) 463419 (Harbour Office)

Type:	wide concrete slipway
Suits:	all craft: trailer-sailers must be rigged clear of the slip and turning area
Availability:	all states of tide, but seek advice at or near LW or if over 25' LOA
Restrictions:	10 knot speed limit in harbour; water skiing permitted in designated area under licence only; jet skis require transit permit; divers require permission
Facilities:	fuel, parking for car nearby and for trailer on site(c), toilets on site, pub adjacent
Dues:	approx. £4.65 (annual fee £19)
Charge:	no additional fee
Directions:	from A27 follow signs to Hayling Is, going to seafront and then turning right and following road to end; site is on western tip of island and adjacent Harbour Office and Ferry Boat Inn
Waters accessed:	Langstone Harbour and The Solent

Hayling Island - Sandy Point
Tel: (0705) 463572 (Sparkes Yacht Harbour Ltd. 38 Wittering Rd)

Type:	launching by crane only
Suits:	all craft up to 45' LOA
Availability:	by prior arrangement on weekdays only
Restrictions:	8 knot speed limit in harbour: water-skiing prohibited; tides run very strongly in the harbour especially in the narrow entrance
Facilities:	fuel, parking for car and trailer (c), toilets, showers, chandlery and boatyard facilities
Dues:	approx. £2.80
Charge:	approx.£13.50 per m
Directions:	from A27 Portsmouth-Chichester Rd take A3023 signposted Hayling Island: site is on east of island after 2 miles, close to Hayling Island SC
Waters accessed:	Chichester Harbour and The Solent

Hayling Island - Hayling Yacht Co Ltd, Mill Rythe Lane
Tel: (0705) 463592

Type:	concrete slipway
Suits:	all craft
Availability:	approx. 2 hours either side HW during daylight hours: phone to make sure slipway is unobstructed
Restrictions:	8 knot speed limit in harbour: water-skiing is prohibited
Facilities:	diesel on site, petrol nearby, parking for car and trailer on site, toilets, chandlery and full boatyard facilities
Dues:	approx. £2.80
Charge:	approx. £6
Directions:	follow signs to Hayling Is from A27, crossing bridge and following main road for 2 miles; after two pubs entrance is 300 yds on left
Waters accessed:	Chichester Harbour and The Solent

Hayling Island - Northney Marina
Tel: (0705) 466321

Type:	concrete slipway
Suits:	all craft especially trailer-sailers
Availability:	all states of tide
Restrictions:	8 knot speed limit in harbour: water-skiing prohibited in harbour
Facilities:	diesel on site, petrol nearby, parking for car and trailer on site, toilets, chandlery, outboard repairs and all yard facilities, bar and restaurant all available on site
Dues:	approx. £2.80
Charge:	approx. £7.05
Directions:	from M27/A27 turn off to Hayling Is turning left immediately after crossing bridge into Northney Road
Waters accessed:	Chichester Harbour and The Solent

Langstone - Ship Inn
Tel: (0243) 512301 (Harbour Office, Itchenor)

Type:	concrete slipway
Suits:	small craft only
Availability:	approx. 3 hours either side HW
Restrictions:	8 knot speed limit in harbour: water-skiing prohibited
Facilities:	fuel from garage over bridge, parking for car and trailer, toilets in pub
Dues:	approx. £2.80
Charge:	no separate fee
Directions:	from M27/A27 turn off onto A3023 to Hayling Is turning left immediately before bridge: site is adjacent to the 'Ship Inn'
Waters accessed:	Chichester Harbour and The Solent

Emsworth - Warblington Road
Tel: (0243) 512301 (Harbour Office, Itchenor)

Type:	shingle hard
Suits:	small craft only
Availability:	approx. 3 hours either side HW
Restrictions:	8 knot speed limit in harbour: water-skiing prohibited
Facilities:	limited parking and turning in road, toilets and chandlery nearby
Dues:	approx. £2.80
Charge:	no separate fee
Directions:	from A27 Portsmouth-Chichester Rd turn off just west of Emsworth into Warblington Rd: site is at end of road
Waters accessed:	Chichester Harbour and The Solent

Emsworth - South Street
Tel: (0243) 512301 (Harbour Office, Itchenor)

Type:	concrete slipway onto shingle
Suits:	all craft
Availability:	approx. 2 hours either side HW
Restrictions:	8 knot speed limit in harbour: water-skiing prohibited
Facilities	parking and toilets in car park at top of street, chandlers opposite
Dues:	approx. £2.80
Charge:	approx. £1.30, pay warden on site
Directions:	from A27 Portsmouth-Chichester Rd turn off into Emsworth
Waters accessed:	Chichester Harbour and The Solent

Emsworth - Tarquin Yacht Harbour Ltd, Thorney Rd
Tel: (0243) 375211

Type:	concrete slipway with winch up to 2½ tons
Suits:	all craft
Availability:	approx. 2½ hours either side HW by prior arrangement
Restrictions:	8 knot speed limit in harbour: water-skiing prohibited
Facilities:	diesel, parking for car and trailer (c), toilets, showers, engine repairs
Dues:	approx. £2.80
Charge:	approx. £2.60 per ft
Directions:	from A27 Portsmouth-Chichester Rd turn off east of Emsworth and follow signs: site is at the north end of Thorney Is
Waters accessed:	Chichester Harbour and The Solent

Prinsted
Tel: (0243) 512301 (Harbour Office, Itchenor)

Type:	shingle hard
Suits:	small craft only
Availability:	approx. 2-3 hours either side HW
Restrictions:	8 knot speed limit in harbour: water-skiing prohibited
Facilities:	no fuel, limited parking for car and trailer, chandlery in Emsworth
Dues:	approx. £2.80
Charge:	no separate fee
Directions:	from A27 Portsmouth-Chichester Rd turn off east of Emsworth: site is at end of road south of the village
Waters accessed:	Chichester Harbour and The Solent

Bosham - Bosham Lane
Tel: (0243) 512301 (Harbour Office, Itchenor)

Type:	shingle hard
Suits:	small craft only
Availability:	approx. 3 hours either side HW
Restrictions:	8 knot speed limit in harbour: water-skiing prohibited
Facilities:	no fuel, parking for car and trailer (c) and toilets in car park nearby
Dues:	approx. £2.80
Charge:	no separate fee
Directions:	from Chichester follow A27, turning onto A259 and following signs: site is at the end of Bosham Lane
Waters accessed:	Chichester Harbour and The Solent

Bosham - The Quay
Tel: (0243) 573336 (Quaymaster)

Type:	concrete slipway
Suits:	all craft
Availability:	all states of tide
Restrictions:	8 knot speed limit in harbour: water-skiing prohibited
Facilities:	no fuel, limited parking on quay, parking for car and trailer (c) and toilets in car park in Bosham Lane
Dues:	approx. £2.80
Charge:	approx. £3.40 or £28 pa
Directions:	from Chichester follow A27, turning onto A259 and following signs: site is on the Quay and access is often congested
Waters accessed:	Chichester Harbour and The Solent

Dell Quay
Tel: (0243) 512301 (Harbour Office, Itchenor)

Type:	shingle hard
Suits:	small craft only
Availability:	approx. 2½ hours either side HW
Restrictions:	8 knot speed limit in harbour: water-skiing prohibited
Facilities:	no fuel, limited parking for car and trailer, pub
Dues:	approx. £2.80
Charge:	no separate fee
Directions:	from Chichester follow A27, turning onto A286 and following signs: site is at the end of road adjacent to Quay
Waters accessed:	Chichester Harbour and The Solent

Birdham - Chichester Yacht Basin
Tel: (0243) 512731

Type:	concrete slipway into locked marina basin
Suits:	all powered craft with less than 4' draft
Availability:	all states of tide although access from locked basin is restricted at LWS; contact basin office or lock control on arrival
Restrictions:	8 knot speed limit in harbour: water-skiing prohibited
Facilities:	fuel, parking for car and trailer, toilets, chandlery, yard facilities, bar all available on site; outboard repairs from Ted Bailey at Itchenor
Dues:	approx. £2.80
Charge:	approx. £11
Directions:	take the A286 off the A27 Chichester bypass signposted to E/W Wittering, turning right to Yacht Basin after 2 miles
Waters accessed:	Chichester Harbour and the Solent

Itchenor
Tel: (0243) 512301 (Harbour Office)

Type:	large shingle hard
Suits:	all craft: best public site in harbour
Availability:	all states of tide
Restrictions:	8 knot speed limit in harbour: water-skiing prohibited
Facilities:	diesel, parking for car and trailer in car park (c), toilets, chandlers, outboard repairs and boatyard nearby
Dues:	approx. £2.80: pay Warden on site
Charge:	approx. £1.30: pay Warden on site
Directions:	take the A286 off the A27 Chichester bypass to E/W Wittering, turning off to Itchenor after 8 miles: site is at end of road
Waters accessed:	Chichester Harbour and the Solent

Bracklesham

Type:	concrete slipway onto shingle beach
Suits:	all craft
Availability:	all states of tide
Restrictions:	8 knot speed limit within 300m MLWS mark with access lane for water-skiing; vehicles other than licensed tractors not permitted on beach
Facilities:	fuel nearby, parking for car and trailer, toilets, cafe
Dues:	none
Charge:	none
Directions:	take the A286 off the A27 Chichester Bypass signposted to E/W Wittering, turning onto B2198: turn left at end of road into East Bracklesham Drive and access is through car park
Waters accessed:	Bracklesham Bay

Selsey - East Beach Amenity Ramp

Type:	wooden ramp over shingle beach may be covered with shingl
Suits:	small craft which can be manhadled only
Availability:	approx. 2-3 hours either side HW or at all times over beach
Restrictions:	8 knot speed limit within 300m from MLWS mark with buoyed access channel: pwc prohibited; there are strong currents in this area and site is not suitable for launching in onshore winds
Facilities:	fuel from garage, parking for car and trailer, toilets, cafe
Dues:	none
Charge:	none
Directions:	from A27 take B2145 and B2201: site is signposted from main street and access is through large car park
Waters accessed:	English Channel

Bognor Regis - Gloucester Road
Tel: (0903) 716133 (Foreshore Officer)

Type:	wide concrete ramp with wooden sides ono sand
Suits:	all craft
Availability:	all states of tide 0800 - 2000 daily
Restrictions:	8 knot speed limit in buoyed area within 300m of MLW mark: water-skiing permitted outside this area
Facilities:	fuel from garage (not sun), parking for car and trailer (c), toilets, chandlers nearby
Dues:	none
Charge:	approx. £6 self launch; £12 assisted
Directions:	from Chichester follow A27 east turning onto A259 and B2166 and following signs to seafront: site is at east end and access is via car park

Waters accessed: English Channel

Littlehampton- Littlehampton Marina, Ferry Road
Tel: (0903) 713553

Type:	launching by yard staff only
Suits:	all craft
Availability:	approx 4 hours either side HW by prior arrangement
Restrictions:	6½ knot speed limit in river: board sailing, water-skiing and pwc prohibited; insurance certificate required for craft; tides run very strongly in river entrance
Facilities:	fuel, parking for car and trailer, toilets, showers, crane, chandlery, diving and boatyard facilities
Dues:	approx. £4
Charge:	approx. £15.60, mon - fri except Bank Holidays; sat, sun and Bank Holidays £19.50
Directions:	from Chichester follow A27 east to Arundel, taking the A284 then A259; cross river and turn left after ½ mile: site is on west bank downstream of bridge and approx. 1 mile from the sea

Waters accessed: River Arun (navigable for 24 miles) and open sea

Ford - Ship and Anchor Marina
Tel: (0243) 551262

Type:	concrete slipway
Suits:	small craft
Availability:	approx. 4 hours either side HW
Restrictions:	launching by yard staff only using tractor at owner's risk; tides in river entrance run strongly
Facilities:	parking for car and trailer, toilet
Dues:	approx, £4
Charge:	yes
Directions:	from the A27 at Arundel take the Ford road: site is after the station

Waters accessed: River Arun (navigable for 24 miles) and open sea

Pulborough - Swan Corner

Type:	steep concrete slipway with snatch block
Suits:	craft up to 15' LOA
Availability:	near HW only
Restrictions:	6 knot speed limit: access is narrow and difficult
Facilities:	limited parking here or at station nearby (c), toilets nearby, pub
Dues:	none
Charge:	none
Directions:	turn off the A29 Bognor road at junction with A283: site is adjacent east side of bridge on north bank

Waters accessed: River Arun (navigable for 24 miles) and open sea

Littlehampton - Fisherman's Quay, Surrey Street>
Tel: (0903) 721215 (Harbour Office)

Type:	steep concrete slipway(1:7) with sharp lip at summit onto mud
Suits:	all craft
Availability:	all states of tide but concrete only extends to half tide mark and thereafter is compacted mud: beware strong currents in river entrance especially at springs
Restrictions:	6½ knot speed limit in harbour and river: water-skiing, board sailing and pwc prohibited in harbour and river
Facilities:	fuel nearby, parking for car and trailer under 14' long on site (c), chandlery, diving supplies and outboard repairs adjacent
Dues:	approx. £4
Charge:	no additional fee
Directions:	follow A284 from Arundel and signs to town centre: site is at end of Surrey St on east bank of river adjacent to Lifeboat Station

Waters accessed: River Arun (navigable for 24 miles) and open sea

Worthing - Sea Place Car Park, Marine Crescent
Tel:(0903) 238977

Type:	steep wooden ramp onto shingle beach
Suits:	small craft which can be manhandled
Availability:	approx. 3 hours either side HW
Restrictions:	8 knot speed limit within buoyed area: slipway has locked barrier and access has height restriction of 4'6"; car park is very congested in summer; no vehicles allowed on Promenade
Facilities:	fuel nearby, parking for car and trailer on site (c), toilets
Dues:	none
Charge:	none
Directions:	follow seafront road approx. 2½ miles west from town centre

Waters accessed: English Channel

Worthing - Alinora Car Park, Marine Crescent
Tel: (0903) 238977 (Beach Office)

Type:	steep wooden ramp onto shingle beach
Suits:	small craft which can be manhandled only
Availability:	approx. 3 hours either side HW
Restrictions:	8 knot speed limit within buoyed area: slipway has locked barrier and access is through car park with 5' height restriction which can be very congested in summer; no vehicles allowed on Promenade
Facilities:	fuel nearby, parking for car and trailer on site (c), toilets nearby
Dues:	none
Charge:	none
Directions:	follow seafront road west for approx. 3 miles from town centre
Waters access:	English Channel

Shoreham Beach - Emerald Quay
Tel: (0273) 592613 (Port Office)

Type:	concrete slipway
Suits:	dinghies and small power craft
Availability:	approx. 2 hours either side HW
Restrictions:	10 mph speed limit in harbour: water-skiing permitted in designated area in river but prohibited in Port waters; jet skis prohibited
Facilities:	fuel nearby, limited parking for car and trailer adjacent or in car park (c) nearby
Dues:	approx. £3.30 per month or £16.90 pa
Charge:	no separate fee
Directions:	turn off A259 after crossing Norfolk Bridge and follow signs to Shoreham Beach: site is off Riverside Rd just before Emerald Quay Housing Estate
Waters accessed:	River Adur,Shoreham Harbour and English Channel

Shoreham - Ropetackle, Little High Street Hard
Tel: (0273) 592613 (Harbour Office)

Type:	tarmac road onto shingle and mud
Suits:	dinghies and small powerboats
Availability:	approx. 2-3 hours either side HW
Restrictions:	10 mph speed limit: water-skiing permitted in designated area upstream but not in Port waters; jet skis prohibited
Facilities:	fuel, parking for car and trailer (c), chandlers and boatyard nearby
Dues:	approx. £3.30 per month; £16.90 pa
Charge:	no separate fee
Directions:	from A24 take A283 to Shoreham turning right after Ballamys' Garage into Little High St: site is upstream of the Norfolk Bridge
Waters accessed:	River Adur, Shoreham Harbour and English Channel

Shoreham Harbour- Just Boats, Half Tide Quay, Albion Street
Tel: (0273) 597222

Type:	concrete slipway
Suits:	all craft up to 25' LOA
Availability:	all states for most craft
Restrictions:	10 mph speed limit in harbour: water-skiing, jet skis and wind-surfers prohibited in Port waters
Facilities:	fuel nearby, parking for car nearby and for trailer on site, toilets, chandlery, outboard repairs and refreshments on site, diving supplies available nearby
Dues:	approx. £3.30 per month; £16.90 pa
Charge:	approx. £15
Directions:	turn off main coast road between Brighton and Worthing (A259) opposite Shoreham Harbour entrance, into Albion St
Waters accessed:	Shoreham Harbour, River Adur and English Channel

Shoreham Harbour - Lady Bee Marina, Albion Street
Tel: (0273) 593801

Type:	concrete and steel slipway into locked harbour
Suits:	shallow-draught craft
Availability:	during normal business hours but subject to lock gates opening on demand within 4 hours either side HW
Restrictions:	10 mph speed limit in harbour: water-skiing and pwc prohibited, telephone to check availability
Facilities:	fuel nearby, limited parking for cars only, toilets, chandlery, showers
Dues:	approx. £21.38 per month; £210.15 pa
Charge:	approx. £5
Directions:	turn off main coast road between Brighton and Worthing (A259) opposite Shoreham Harbour entrance into Albion St
Waters accessed:	Shoreham Harbour, River Adur and English Channel

Newhaven - Newhaven Marina
Tel: (0273) 513881 (David Bourne or Rosemarie Bond)

Type:	concrete slipway: all launching and recovery carried out by yard staff with tractor
Suits:	craft up to 20' LOA: no pwc
Availability:	3-4 hours either side HW from 0800 -1700: check for availability
Restrictions:	5 knot speed limit in harbour: pwc prohibited
Facilities:	diesel on site, petrol nearby, parking for car and trailer, toilets and showers, chandlery, cafe, outboard repairs, yacht club all on site
Dues:	no separate charge
Charge:	approx. £25 inc harbour dues; season ticket available

Directions: follow M23/A23 to Brighton, then A259 coast road 7 miles to
Newhaven: site is on west bank of river
Waters accessed: River Ouse and English Channel

Newhaven Harbour - Riverside Road, West Side
Tel: (0273) 514131 (ask for Duty Supervisor)

Type: concrete slipway
Suits: all craft except pwc
Availability: tides above 5m
Restrictions: 5 knot speed limit in harbour: pwc prohibited; approach to site can
be congested; this is a busy fishing and ferry harbour
Facilities: diesel on site, petrol nearby, parking for car and trailer nearby,
chandlery, diving supplies and outboard repairs all on site
Dues: none
Charge: none
Directions: turn off A259 coast road following signs to Newhaven: site is on
west side of harbour near fishing jetty No.11
Waters accessed: River Ouse and English Channel

Eastbourne - Prince William Parade
Tel: (0323) 412260

Type: launching over steeply sloping shingle beach
Suits: small craft which can be manhandled
Availability: most states of tide
Restrictions: 8 knot speed limit within 100yds of shore: distance to water may be
considerable at LW; access has 7'3" height restriction
Facilities: parking for car and trailer on site, chandlery and outboard repairs
nearby
Dues: none
Charge: none
Directions: turn east on Eastbourne seafront and take last exit at large round-
about going along Prince William Parade, then turn right under
metal archway and up onto beach
Waters accessed: English Channel

Bexhill-on-Sea - West Parade
Tel: (0424) 212023 ext. 31

Type: concrete slipway onto shingle beach
Suits: small craft which can be manhandled
Availability: approx. 3 hours either side HW
Restrictions: 8 knot speed limit within 100yds of shore with access lanes for
water-skiing; vehicles are not allowed on the promenade
Facilities: fuel (½ mile), parking for car and trailer on site, toilets and cafe
nearby
Dues: none

Charge: none
Directions: follow signs to seafront from A259
Waters accessed: English Channel

Rye Harbour - Rye Harbour Village
Tel: (0797) 225225 (Harbour Master)

Type: concrete slipway
Suits: all craft
Availability: approx. 2 hours before HW to 3 hours after
Restrictions: 6 knot speed limit in river: pwc are restricted and water-skiing in river for club members only; narrow harbour entrance with bar and strong tidal flow: vessels must not enter or leave harbour against the direction of the Harbour Master
Facilities: fuel nearby, parking for car and trailer on site, toilets, chandlery, pub, sailing club, shop, yard facilities and ouboard repairs nearby
Dues: approx. £8.75
Charge: no additional fee
Directions: follow A259 to Rye and then signs to Rye Harbour
Waters accessed: River Rother and the English Channel

New Romney - Varne Boat Club, Littlestone-on-Sea
Tel: (0679) 62993 (Clubhouse) or (0622) 737359 (Membership Sec.)

Type: assisted launching from concrete slipway
Suits: all craft up to 25' LOA
Availability: approx. 3 hours either side HW by prior arrangement
Restrictions: speed limit inside marker buoys: water skiing permitted in designated area
Facilities: fuel (1 mile), parking for car and trailer, toilets and showers, changing rooms and refreshments
Dues: none
Charge: approx. £12 with assistance
Directions: follow A259 to New Romney turning right onto the B2071 to Littlestone-on-Sea: turn right to Greatstone-on-Sea and the club is on the left
Waters accessed: Romney Bay and the English Channel

Folkestone - Inner Harbour Slipway
Tel: (0303) 220544 (Port Office)

Type: concrete slipway
Suits: all craft
Availability: approx. 2-3 hours either side HW: report to small cafe adjacent to site to pay fee
Restrictions: 5 mph speed limit in inner Harbour: access to site restricted by narrow and low arches
Facilities: fuel, parking for car and trailer, toilets, chandlery, diving supplies,

outboard repairs and other facilities all available nearby

Dues: approx. £2.50
Charge: no additional fee
Directions: from M20/A20 follow signs to Folkestone Harbour
Waters accessed: Folkestone Harbour and the English Channel

Dover - The Promenade
Tel: (0304) 240400 ext. 4535 (Marine Services Officer)

Type: steep concrete slipway onto beach
Suits: craft which can be manhandled
Availability: all times
Restrictions: 8 knot speed limit in harbour: due to constant shipping movements, craft are not allowed to enter east of the reclaim or go to northern edge of anchorage; craft wishing to leave by east or west entrance must contact Port Control on Ch 74,12 or16 call sign 'Dover Port Control'
Facilities: diesel from barge in Outer Harbour, petrol nearby, parking for car nearby (but not on Promenade) and for trailer on site, toilets, chandlery, outboard repairs nearby, diving supplies from clock tower at west end of promenade
Dues: none
Charge: none
Directions: follow A2 to Eastern Docks, then along Marine Parade: site is opposite Royal Cinque Ports YC
Waters accessed: Dover Harbour and the English Channel

St Margaret's-at-Cliffe
Tel: (0304) 821199 (Recreation Officer)

Type: wooden ramp onto beach is often covered by shingle
Suits: small craft which can be manhandled
Availability: all states of tide but best at HW
Restrictions: 10 mph speed limit within 150m of LW mark with access lane: site may be crowded
Facilities: no fuel, parking for car and trailer (c), toilets, refreshments
Dues: none
Charge: none
Directions: from Dover follow A2 to top of Jubilee Way turning onto A258 to Deal; turn right onto B2058 to St Margaret's
Waters accessed: St Margaret's Bay and English Channel

Deal - Kingsdown

Tel: (0304) 821199 (Recreation Officer)

Type:	wooden ramp onto shingle with dog leg access
Suits:	small craft which can be manhandled
Availability:	all states of tide but best at HW
Restrictions:	10mph speed limit within 150m of LW mark with access channels for water-skiing
Facilities:	limited parking for car and trailer, no toilets
Dues:	none
Charge:	none
Directions:	from Dover follow A2 to top of Jubilee Way turning onto A258 to Deal; turn right onto B2057 to Kingsdown
Waters accessed:	Dover Strait and English Channel

Deal - North End Ramps

Tel: (0304) 821199 (Recreation Officer)

Type:	2 concrete slipways
Suits:	small craft which can be manhandled: no cars on Promenade
Availability:	all states of tide summer only
Restrictions:	10 mph speed limit within 150m of LW mark: water-skiing with access channels permitted outside this area; access to site closed in winter due to risk of flooding; site may be busy
Facilities:	no fuel, limited parking for cars only
Dues:	none
Charge:	none
Directions:	from Dover follow A2 to top of Jubilee Way turning onto A258 to Deal: site is accessed from the Promenade
Waters accessed:	Dover Strait and English Channel

Sandwich - Town Quay

Tel: (0304) 821199 (Recreation Officer)

Type:	concrete slipway
Suits:	craft up tp 20' LOA
Availability:	approx. 2 hours either side HW
Restrictions:	6 mph speed limit in river, water-skiing permitted in open sea
Facilities:	fuel from local garage, parking for car and trailer (c), toilets, chandlery and boatyard facilities nearby
Dues:	none
Charge:	none
Directions:	from Canterbury follow A257 east then signs to town centre
Waters accessed:	River Stour and Pegwell Bay

Ramsgate - Western Undercliff
Tel: (0843) 225511 ext 2560 (Water Safety Officer)

Type:	concrete slipway
Suits:	small powered craft
Availability:	approx. 2 hours either side HW
Restrictions:	speed limit near shore: water-skiing permitted in designated area: pwc prohibited; access to site is via narrow road
Facilities:	no fuel, parking for car and trailer on site (c), toilets,
Dues:	none
Charge:	none
Directions:	from town centre take Royal Parade to St Augustine's Rd then go along Royal Esplanade to the Putting Green

Waters accessed: English Channel

Broadstairs - Harbour Slipway

Type:	concrete slipway and wooden slipway
Suits:	all craft
Availability:	approx. 2½ hours either side HW
Restrictions:	5 knot speed limit in harbour and 8 knot speed limit within 400m of HW mark
Facilities:	fuel from garage (½ mile), parking for car and trailer, toilets
Dues:	not known
Charge:	yes
Directions:	from Margate or Ramsgate follow A255

Waters accessed: English Channel

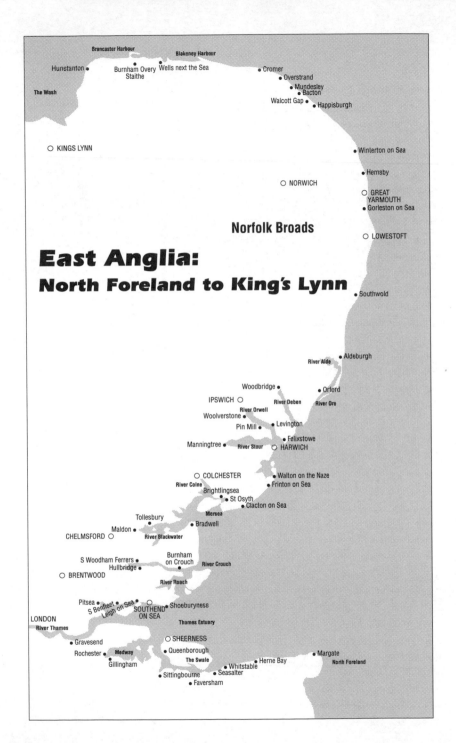

Brancaster Harbour

Blakeney Harbour

Hunstanton •
Burnham Overy
Staithe
• Wells next the Sea

Cromer
• Overstrand
• Mundesley
• Bacton
Walcott Gap • • Happisburgh

The Wash

○ KINGS LYNN

• Winterton on Sea

• Hemsby

○ NORWICH

○ GREAT
YARMOUTH
• Gorleston on Sea

Norfolk Broads

○ LOWESTOFT

East Anglia:
North Foreland to King's Lynn

• Southwold

• Aldeburgh
River Alde

Woodbridge •
• Orford
IPSWICH ○
River Deben   River Ore
River Orwell
Woolverstone •
Pin Mill • • Levington
• Felixstowe
Manningtree • River Stour ○ HARWICH

○ COLCHESTER
• Walton on the Naze
River Colne   • Frinton on Sea
Brightlingsea
• St Osyth
Mersea   • Clacton on Sea
Tollesbury •
Maldon • • Bradwell
CHELMSFORD ○ River Blackwater

S Woodham Ferrers • Burnham
Hullbridge • on Crouch River Crouch
○ BRENTWOOD
River Roach

Pitsea •
S Benfleet • • • Shoeburyness
Leigh on Sea ○
LONDON SOUTHEND
River Thames ON SEA Thames Estuary

○ SHEERNESS
• Gravesend
Rochester • • Queenborough • Margate
Medway The Swale North Foreland
Gillingham • • Herne Bay
• Whitstable
• Sittingbourne • Seasalter
• Faversham

84

Margate - Palm Bay (Foreness Bay)

Tel: (0843) 225511 ext. 2560 (Foreshore and Recreation Officer)

Type:	concrete slipway onto beach
Suits:	powered craft only
Availability:	all states of tide but best 2 hours either side HW
Restrictions:	this is a designated water-skiing area operated by Foreness Ski Club; other activities are not permitted
Facilities:	fuel from garage (1 mile), parking for car and trailer, toilets
Dues:	none
Charge:	none
Directions:	from Canterbury follow A28 to Cliftonville seafront, east of Margate town centre
Waters accessed:	Thames Estuary

Margate - Harbour Slip

Tel: (0843) 225511 ext 2560 (Foreshore and Recreation Officer)

Type:	concrete slipway onto sand
Suits:	small powered craft
Availability:	approx. 2 hours either side HW
Restrictions:	8 knot speed limit within 400m HW mark: water-skiing permitted in designated area
Facilities:	no fuel, parking for car and trailer (c) and toilets on site; chandlery, diving supplies and repairs available nearby; Margate YC adjacent
Dues:	none
Charge:	none
Directions:	from Canterbury follow A28 to town centre and signs to harbour
Waters accessed:	Thames Estuary

Margate - Westbrook Bay

Tel: (0843) 225511 ext 2560 (Foreshore and Recreation Officer)

Type:	concrete slipway onto firm sand
Suits:	small powered craft
Availability:	approx. 2 hours either side HW
Restrictions:	speed limit: this is a designated water-skiing area, other activities are not permitted
Facilities:	no fuel, parking for car and trailer on site; repairs available nearby
Dues:	none
Charge:	none
Directions:	from Canterbury follow A28 to Margate and take coast road west
Waters accessed:	Thames Estuary

Margate - St Mildreds Bay
Tel: (0843) 225511 ext 2560 (Foreshore and Recreation Officer)

Type:	concrete slipway onto firm sand
Suits:	sailing dinghies, trailer-sailers and small powered craft up to 15hp
Availability:	approx. 2 hours either side HW
Restrictions:	speed limit: water-skiing and large powered craft prohibited; vehicles are not allowed on the beach
Facilities:	no fuel, parking for car and trailer (c) and toilets on site, repairs available nearby
Dues:	none
Charge:	none
Directions:	from Margate follow A28 towards Canterbury: turn right into Westbrook Ave. then right again into St Mildreds Ave.
Waters accessed:	Thames Estuary

Margate - West Bay, Westgate, East Ramp
Tel: (0843) 225511 ext 2560 (Foreshore and Recreation Officer)

Type:	concrete slipway onto firm sand
Suits:	sailing dinghies, trailer-sailers and small powered craft up to 15hp, windsurfers and canoes
Availability:	approx. 2 hours either side HW
Restrictions:	speed limit: water-skiing and large powered craft prohibited
Facilities:	parking for car and trailer and toilets on site, repairs nearby
Dues:	none
Charge:	none
Directions:	from Margate follow A28 towards Canterbury: turn right into Westbrook Ave and at end of road turn right onto West Bay
Waters accessed:	Thames Estuary

Margate - Beresford Gap, Birchington
Tel: (0843) 225511 ext 2560 (Foreshore and Recreation Officer)

Type:	steep concrete slipway onto Promenade
Suits:	speed boats only
Availability:	approx. 2 hours either side HW
Restrictions:	this is a designated water-skiing area, other activities are not permitted
Facilities:	no fuel, parking for car and trailer on site
Dues:	none
Charge:	none
Directions:	from Canterbury follow A28 east: at Birchington town square take Station Rd to Minnis Bay turn right along Coast Rd towards Margate
Waters accessed:	Thames Estuary

Margate - Minnis Bay, Birchington
Tel: (0843) 225511 ext 2560 (Foreshore and Recreation Officer)

Type:	concrete slipway onto firm sand
Suits:	sailing dinghies, trailer-sailers and small powered craft up to 15hp
Availability:	approx. 2 hours either side HW
Restrictions:	speed limit: water-skiing, large powered craft and jet skis prohibited
Facilities:	parking for car and trailer and cafe on site, toilets nearby
Dues:	none
Charge:	none
Directions:	from Canterbury follow A28 east: at Birchington town square take Station Rd to Minnis Bay

Waters accessed: Thames Estuary

Herne Bay - Neptune Jetty, Central Parade
Tel: (0227) 763763

Type:	concrete slipway
Suits:	all craft
Availability:	approx. 3 hours either side HW
Restrictions:	8 knot speed limit within 300m of shore: water-skiing permitted outside this area; site is exposed in northerly winds
Facilities:	fuel (½ mile), limited parking for car and trailer (c) and toilets on site, outboard repairs (½ mile): water safety patrol boat in operation
Dues:	none
Charge:	none
Directions:	leave M2 at junction 7 and follow A299 to Herne Bay then signs to seafront; site is east of Pier near Clock Tower

Waters accessed: Thames Estuary

Herne Bay - Breakwater Slipway, Central Parade
Tel: (0227) 763763

Type:	concrete slipway
Suits:	all craft
Availability:	approx. 2½ hours either side HW
Restrictions:	8 knot speed limit within 300m of shore: water-skiing permitted outside this area but pwc prohibited at this site: site is exposed in northerly winds
Facilities:	fuel (½ mile), parking for car and trailer (c) and toilets on site, outboard repairs (½ mile): water safety patrol boat in operation
Dues:	none
Charge:	none
Directions:	leave M2 at junction 7 and follow A299 to Herne Bay then signs to seafront

Waters accessed: Thames Estuary

Herne Bay - Hampton Slipway, Swalecliffe Avenue
Tel: (0227) 763763

Type:	concrete slipway with stepped slope onto mud and shingle
Suits:	all craft
Availability:	approx. 2½ hours either side HW
Restrictions:	8 knot speed limit within 300m of shore: this is a designated water-ski area with buoyed access lane from slipway
Facilities:	fuel from garage (½ mile), parking for car and trailer and toilets on site, outboard repairs (¾ mile): water safety patrol boat in operation
Dues:	none
Charge:	none
Directions:	follow B2205 west from Herne Bay, turning from Hampton Pier Ave into Swalecliffe Ave
Waters accessed:	Thames Estuary

Whitstable - West Quay Slipway, Whitstable Harbour
Tel: (0227) 274086

Type:	concrete slipway
Suits:	all craft
Availability:	approx. 2½ hours either side HW
Restrictions:	8 knot speed limit within 300m of shore: water-skiing permitted outside this area
Facilities:	fuel from garage (¼ mile), parking for car and trailer (200yds) (c), toilets nearby, chandlery and outboard repairs (300m): water safety patrol boat in operation
Dues:	none
Charge:	none
Direction:	leave M2 at junction 7 following A299 to Whitstable then turn off towards sea and follow coast road to harbour
Waters accessed:	Thames Estuary

Whitstable - Sea Wall (The Dinghy Store)
Tel: (0227) 274168

Type:	concrete slipway onto shingle
Suits:	all craft including jet skis and windsurfers
Availability:	approx. 3 hours either side HW
Restrictions:	8 knot speed limit within 300m of shore: water-skiing permitted outside this area
Facilities:	fuel nearby, parking for car and trailer and toilets nearby, chandlery and outboard repairs available on site
Dues:	none
Charge:	none
Directions:	from M2 follow A299/A290: site is on sea wall just W of harbour
Waters accessed:	Thames Estuary

Seasalter - Alberta Car Park

Type:	launch over steep shingle bank onto sandy beach
Suits:	small craft
Availability:	HW only
Restrictions:	8 knot speed limit within 300m of shore: water-skiing permitted in designated areas only
Facilities:	no fuel, parking for car and trailer (c)
Dues:	none
Charge:	none
Directions:	from M2 follow A299 turning off west of Whitstable following signs to Seasalter: site is accessed through public car park adjacent Seasalter Water Ski Club
Waters accessed:	Thames Estuary

Harty Ferry - Old Ferry Slipway

Type:	concrete slipway onto shingle
Suits:	all craft
Availability:	approx. 2-3 hours either side HW or all states of tide for dinghies
Restrictions:	8 knot speed limit inshore: water-skiing prohibited
Facilities:	no fuel, limited parking for car and trailer
Dues:	none
Charge:	none
Directions:	leave M2 at junction 6 following signs to Oare then Harty Ferry two miles north of Faversham
Waters accessed:	The Swale and Thames Estuary

Conyer - Swale Marina, Conyer Wharf, Teynham
Tel: (0795) 521562

Type:	concrete slipway
Suits:	all craft
Availability:	approx. 2-3 hours either side HW
Restrictions:	8 knot speed limit inshore: water-skiing prohibited
Facilities:	diesel on site,parking for car and trailer (c), toilets and showers, chandlery and other boatyard facilities all on site
Dues:	none
Charge:	yes
Directions:	from Sittingbourne follow A2 east, turn off onto minor roads and follow signs
Waters accessed:	Conyer Creek, The Swale and Thames Estuary

Sittingbourne - Kingsferry Bridge

Type:	concrete slipway
Suits:	all craft
Availability:	approx. 2 hours either side HW
Restrictions:	8 knot speed limit: water-skiing permitted in Long Reach
Facilities:	no fuel or toilets, parking for car and trailer on site (c)
Dues:	none
Charge:	yes
Directions:	leave M2 at junction 5 following A249 to Isle of Sheppey: site is on mainland side of bridge: follow signs to Ridham Dock
Waters accessed:	The Swale and Thames Estuary

Queenborough, Isle of Sheppey - Queenborough Hard
Tel: (0795) 662051

Type:	concrete slipway onto shingle
Suits:	all craft up to 20' LOA
Availability:	all states of tide
Restrictions:	8 knot speed limit: water-skiing permitted in Long Reach designated area only: diving permitted outside harbour area: access road to site is narrow
Facilities:	fuel nearby, limited parking for car and trailer and toilets on site, chandlery and outboard repairs, shops, pubs and restaurants nearby: temporary membership Queenborough YC available
Dues:	none
Charge:	approx. £5.00
Directions:	leave M2 at junction 5 following A249 to Isle of Sheppey and signs to Sheerness and Queenborough town centre: site is off High St
Waters accessed:	The Swale, River Medway and Thames Estuary

Sheerness, Isle of Sheppey - Barton Point, Marine Parade

Type:	launching over shingle
Suits:	small craft only
Availability:	all states of tide but best near HW
Restrictions:	8 knot speed limit inshore: water-skiing in designated area offshore with access lane
Facilities:	no fuel, parking for car and trailer, toilets nearby
Dues:	none
Charge:	none
Direction:	leave M2 at junction 5 following A249 to Isle of Sheppey and signs to Sheerness: access to site is via Marine Parade
Waters accessed:	Thames Estuary

Minster, Isle of Sheppey

Type:	concrete slipway onto shingle
Suits:	small craft only
Availability:	approx. 2 hours either side HW
Restrictions:	8 knot speed limit inshore: water-skiing in designated area
Facilities:	fuel from local garages, parking for car and trailer (c), toilets
Dues:	none
Charge:	yes
Directions:	leave M2 at junction 5 and follow A249 to Sheerness: at Clock Tower turn right onto Marine Parade and follow for 1¼ miles
Waters accessed:	Thames Estuary

Gillingham - Commodore Hard, The Strand, Lower Rainham Road

Type:	concrete slipway
Suits:	sailing dinghies and other small craft which can be manhandled
Availability:	all states of tide
Restrictions:	6 knot speed limit in river: water-skiing and pwc prohibited: access is via a narrow road and vehicles are not permitted on slipway
Facilities:	fuel nearby, limited parking for car only in public car parks 250-300m away (these car parks can become very congested); no parking for trailers; toilets on site, chandlery nearby
Dues:	none
Charge:	none
Directions:	leave M2 at junction 4 following A278 to A2 and turn right; turn left onto B2004, site is accessed from this road
Waters accessed:	River Medway, The Swale and Thames Estuary

Gillingham - Gillingham Marina
Tel: (0634) 280022

Type:	boat hoist only into locked marina basin
Suits:	trailer-sailers only
Availability:	daylight hours by arrangement only contact the Berthing Manager: access to river via lock approx. 4 hours either side HW
Restrictions:	6 knot speed limit in river
Facilities:	diesel on site, parking for car and trailer, toilets, showers, chandlery and other marina facilities on site
Dues:	none
Charge:	approx. £9.10 per metre for launch and recovery
Directions:	leave M2 at junction 4 following A278 to A2 and turning right; turn left onto B2004, site is accessed via Pier Rd
Waters accessed:	River Medway, The Swale and Thames Estuary

Halling - Elmhaven Marina, Rochester Rd
Tel: (0634) 240489

Type:	steep concrete slipway
Suits:	dinghies and small powered craft
Availability:	approx. 2 hours either side HW during normal working hours by prior arrangement
Restrictions:	6 knot speed limit: water-skiing and pwc prohibited: site is above Rochester Bridge and there is restricted headroom
Facilities:	no fuel, parking for car and trailer, toilets, showers and outboard repairs on site
Dues:	none
Charge:	approx. £5.00
Directions:	leave M2 at junction 2 and follow A228 south through Cuxton to Halling
Waters accessed:	River Medway, The Swale and Thames Estuary

Cuxton - Cuxton Marina, Station Road
Tel: (0634) 721941

Type:	concrete slipway
Suits:	dinghies and small powered craft
Availability:	approx. 2 hours either side HW during normal working hours by prior arrangement
Restrictions:	6 knot speed limit: water-skiing and pwc prohibited; site is above Rochester Bridge and there is restricted headroom
Facilities:	no fuel, parking for car and trailer, toilets and outboard repairs on site, chandlery nearby
Dues:	none
Charge:	approx. £5.00
Directions:	leave M2 at junction 2 and follow A228 south through Cuxton: boatyard is on left
Waters accessed:	River Medway, The Swale and Thames Estuary

Rochester - Medway Bridge Marina, Manor Lane
Tel: (0634) 843576

Type:	launching by marina equipment only
Suits:	trailer-sailers and small powered craft
Availability:	approx. 4 hours either side HW 0900-1700 weekdays only by prior arrangement
Restrictions:	6 knot speed limit: speed boats, water-skiing and pwc prohibited
Facilities:	fuel, parking for car and trailer, toilets, showers, chandlery, repairs, restaurant, bar all on site
Dues:	none
Charge:	approx. £33
Directions:	leave M2 at junction 2, taking A228 north then follow A2 over Rochester town bridge, immediately turning right at traffic lights: go

a short distance up hill to 'T' junction, turn right: take 1st right into Manor Lane and marina is at bottom of steep hill

Waters accessed: River Medway, The Swale and Thames Estuary

Gravesend - Gravesham Marina, Gravesend Promenade
Tel: (0474) 566692

Type:	concrete and wooden ramp
Suits:	all craft
Availability:	at all states of tide: lock into river open for 1 hour before HW
Restrictions:	3 knot speed limit in basin: water-skiing and pwc prohibited
Facilities:	fuel nearby, parking for car nearby and for trailer on site; toilets; chandlery, outboard repairs and engineering nearby; moorings
Dues:	approx.£5.00
Charge:	approx.£5.00 plus £6 tide fee charged for lock opening before 0700 and after 2100 due to tide times
Directions:	from London take A2 following signs to Rochester: at Gravesend east turn off along Valley Drive, turning right into Old Rd East: at roundabout turn left along Rochester Rd to next roundabout then right into Ordnance Rd: site is at bottom of road

Waters accessed: River Thames

Pitsea - Pitsea Hall Country Park, Vange Creek
Tel: (0268) 550088

Type:	steep concrete slipway
Suits:	most craft
Availability:	approx. 2½ hours either side HW by prior arrangement
Restrictions:	8 knot speed limit: water-skiing permitted in designated area in Holehaven Creek; jet bikes permitted in Fobbing Ck by prior arrangement only: 3rd party insurance certificate required
Facilities:	no fuel, parking for car and trailer, toilets and cafe on site
Dues:	none
Charge:	approx. £7
Directions:	Country Park is signposted from A13

Waters accessed: Vange Ck, Holehaven Ck and Thames Estuary

South Benfleet - Benfleet Causeway

Type:	two concrete slipways, one either side of Benfleet Ck barrage
Suits:	all craft
Availability:	approx. 2 hours either side HW
Restrictions:	8 knot speed limit: water-skiing permitted in designated areas at some distance from this site: pwc prohibited
Facilities:	no fuel, parking for car and trailer nearby (c), toilets, chandlery and outboard repairs nearby
Dues:	none

Charge: none
Directions: from Southend follow A127/A13 west towards London: take A130 south to Canvey Island: on island take first left back to Benfleet: sites are immediately on right hand side over bridge
Waters accessed: Benfleet Creek and Thames Estuary

Leigh-on-Sea - Two Tree Island
Tel: (0702) 711010

Type: concrete slipway
Suits: all craft
Availability: approx. 4 hours either side HW
Restrictions: 8 knot speed limit: pwc prohibited; water-skiing permitted in designated areas nearby
Facilities: no fuel, parking for car and trailer and toilets on site, chandlery and outboard repairs nearby
Dues: none
Charge: approx. £7.80
Directions: from Southend follow A13 to Leigh-on-Sea, turning off at railway station into Marsh Rd: site is approx. 1 mile down road
Waters accessed: Thames Estuary

Leigh-on-Sea - Old High Street
Tel: (0702) 710561

Type: concrete slipway
Suits: dinghies and small trailer-sailers
Availability: approx. 2 hours either side HW
Restrictions: 8 knot speed limit: water-skiing permitted in designated areas: pwc prohibited; access is via narrow busy High St
Facilities: fuel nearby, parking for car nearby (c), no parking for trailer, toilets on site, chandlery and outboard repairs nearby in 'Old Leigh'
Dues: none
Charge: none
Directions: from Southend follow A13 4 miles to Leigh Old Town turning off 400yds from railway station
Waters accessed: Thames Estuary

Southend-on-Sea - Esplanade
Tel: (0702) 611889 (Foreshore Office, Pier Hill)

Type: concrete slipway onto sand
Suits: small craft which can be manhandled
Availability: approx. 2½ hours either side HW
Restrictions: 8 knot speed limit: water-skiing permitted in designated areas: pwc prohibited: access is via busy seafront road
Facilities: fuel nearby, parking for car and trailer in local car parks (c), no toi-

	lets, chandlery, diving supplies and outboard repairs nearby
Dues:	none
Charge:	none
Directions:	from London follow A13 or A127 to Southend then signs to seafront: site is 1 mile E of Pier
Waters accessed:	Thames Estuary

Shoeburyness - West Beach
Tel: (0702) 293742

Type:	steep concrete slipway onto hard sand
Suits:	all craft
Availability:	approx. 3 hours either side HW
Restrictions:	8 knot speed limit: water-skiing permitted in buoyed area with access corridor: jet skis are prohibited
Facilities:	no fuel, parking for car (c) in public car park nearby and for trailer (c) on site, toilets nearby
Dues:	none
Charge:	approx. £7.80
Directions:	follow A13 four miles east of Southend: site is on seafront opposite the end of Waterford Rd and adjacent Coastguard Station
Waters accessed:	Thames Estuary

Shoeburyness - East Beach Road
Tel: (0702) 293744

Type:	concrete slipway onto hard sand
Suits:	all craft
Availability:	approx. 4 hours either side HW 0900-1600
Restrictions:	8 knot speed limit: water-skiing permitted in buoyed area with access corridor
Facilities:	no fuel, parking for car and trailer (c) on site, toilets
Dues:	none
Charge:	approx. £7.80
Directions:	from Southend follow A13 east for about 5 miles: site is on sea front with access through East Beach car park
Waters accessed:	Thames Estuary

Paglesham - Paglesham Boatyard Ltd, East End
Tel: (0702) 258885

Type:	concrete slipway
Suits:	all craft
Availability:	all states of tide
Restrictions:	8 knot speed limit: pwc prohibited; water-skiing permitted in designated areas in R. Crouch; sea wall gate closed at night in winter
Facilities:	diesel on site, parking for car and trailer, toilets, crane, pub,

	overnight moorings all available on site
Dues:	none
Charge:	approx. £6.00 (put through letterbox if nobody in yard)
Directions:	follow A127 west turning onto B1013 to Rochford: follow minor roads to Stambridge; go through village turning right at 'T' junction then right again by 'Shepherd & Dog'; follow signs to boatyard
Waters accessed:	River Roach, River Crouch and Thames Estuary

Wallasea Island - Essex Marina, Canewdon
Tel: (0702) 258531

Type:	launching by marina staff with marina equipment only
Suits:	craft over 25' LOA
Availability:	during working hours by prior arrangement
Restrictions:	speed limit
Facilities:	fuel, parking for car and trailer (c), toilets, chandlery, showers and other marina facilities all on site
Dues:	yes
Charge:	approx. 25'-34' LOA - £3 17 per ft, 35'-39' LOA - £3 40 per ft other rates on application
Directions:	from London follow A12/A127 to Rayleigh then A129/B1013 north: at Hockley turn onto minor roads following signs to Canewdon
Waters accessed:	River Crouch and Thames Estuary

Hullbridge Ford - Ferry Road
Tel: (0621) 783602 (Harbour Officek, 22 High St, Burnham-on-Crouch)

Type:	launching from tarmac road onto shingle
Suits:	dinghies and small powered craft
Availability:	approx. 2 hours either side HW
Restrictions:	8 knot speed limit: water-skiing permitted but only by special licence; access is via a narrow road and slipway is not maintained below mean HW
Facilities:	no fuel, parking for car and trailer (c) on site
Dues:	approx. £9.00 pa
Charge:	no additional fee
Directions:	from Chelmsford follow A130 south, turning off through Battlesbridge onto minor roads and following signs: site is on south bank of river
Waters accessed:	River Crouch and Thames Estuary

South Woodham Ferrers
Tel: (0621) 783602 (Harbour Office. 22 High St, Burnham-on-Crouch)

Type:	launching over poor shingle and mud surface
Suits:	dinghies and small powered craft
Availability:	approx. 2 hours either side HW
Restrictions:	8 knot speed limit: water-skiing permitted but only by special licence;access is via a narrow road and slipway is not maintained
Facilities:	no fuel, parking for car and trailer (c) on site
Dues:	approx. £9.00 pa
Charge:	none
Directions:	from Chelmsford follow A130 south, turning east onto A132/B1012 and following road past station: site is on north bank of river in Country Park opposite Hullbridge
Waters accessed:	River Crouch and Thames Estuary

Burnham-on-Crouch - Burnham Yacht Harbour, Foundry Lane
Tel: (0621) 782150

Type:	concrete slipway and 30 ton travel hoist and crane
Suits:	all craft except speedboats
Availability:	all states of tide during daylight hours
Restrictions:	8 knot speed limit: water-skiing, speedboats and pwc prohibited
Facilities:	diesel, parking for car and trailer, toilets and showers, chandlery and other marina facilities on site
Dues:	approx. £9.00 pa
Charge:	approx. £6.00
Directions:	from Chelmsford follow A130 south, turning onto A132/B1012 and follow B1010 east to Burnham-on-Crouch: cross over railway bridge and turn right by shops into Foundry Lane
Waters accessed:	River Crouch and Thames Estuary

Bradwell-on-Sea - Port Flair Ltd, Bradwell Marina, Waterside
Tel: (0621) 776235

Type:	two concrete slipways
Suits:	all craft except pwc
Availability:	approx. 4½ hours either side HW after 0830
Restrictions:	8 knot speed limit: boats must leave marina under power; pwc are prohibited: water-skiing is permitted in river in designated areas
Facilities:	fuel, parking for car and trailer, toilets, chandlery, showers, other marina facilities and clubhouse available for visitors on site
Dues:	none
Charge:	approx. £10-13 depending on type of craft
Directions:	from Chelmsford follow A414 to Maldon, then B1018 south to Latchingdon: turn left onto signposted minor roads
Waters accessed:	River Blackwater and Thames Estuary

St Lawrence Bay - The Stone (Ramsey Island)
Tel: (0621) 856487 (River Bailiff, Maldon)

Type:	concrete slipway onto hard sand
Suits:	small craft only
Availability:	all states of tide
Restrictions:	8 knot speed limit: water-skiing permitted in designated areas
Facilities:	fuel in village, very limited parking for car and trailer, toilets nearby
Dues:	none
Charge:	yes
Directions:	from Chelmsford follow A414 to Maldon, then B1018 south to Latchingdon: turn left onto minor roads towards Bradwell-on-Sea; turning left after 6 miles to The Stone

Waters accessed: River Blackwater and Thames Estuary

Maylandsea - Blackwater Marina, Marine Parade
Tel: (0621) 740264

Type:	wide concrete slipway
Suits:	all craft
Availability:	approx. 2-3 hours either side HW 0900-1600 by prior arrangement
Restrictions:	8 knot speed limit: water-skiing permitted in designated areas
Facilities:	diesel on site, petrol nearby, parking for car and trailer, toilets, showers, full workshop all on site: bar/club/restaurant opening summer 1994
Dues:	none
Charge:	approx. £10.00
Directions:	from Chelmsford follow A414 to Maldon, then B1018 south to Latchingdon: turn left onto signposted minor roads and left again after approx. 2½ miles

Waters accessed: River Blackwater and Thames Estuary

Maldon - Promenade Park
Tel: (0621) 856487 (River Bailiff, Maldon)

Type:	concrete slipway
Suits:	all craft up to 20' LOA and max. weight 650 kilos
Availability:	approx. 2 hours either side HW
Restrictions:	8 knot speed limit: water-skiing permitted in designated areas
Facilities:	fuel in town, parking for car and trailer (c) on site, toilets, chandlery and outboard repairs all nearby
Dues:	none
Charge:	none
Directions:	from Chelmsford take A414 to Maldon, follow Maldon southern bypass and signs to Promenade

Waters accessed: River Blackwater and Thames Estuary

Maldon - Maldon Boatyard, North Street

Tel: (0621) 854280

Type:	concrete slipway
Suits:	all craft except pwc
Availability:	approx. 2 hours either side HW 0800-1800 (later in summer) by prior arrangement
Restrictions:	8 knot speed limit: water-skiing permitted in designated areas downstream; pwc prohibited
Facilities:	diesel on site, petrol in town, parking for car and trailer (c) on site, toilets, chandlery, outboard repairs and 6 ton crane on site
Dues:	none
Charge:	approx. £8
Directions:	from Chelmsford take A414 to Maldon High St: continue down High St turning left into North St: site is at bottom of street

Waters accessed: River Blackwater and Thames Estuary

Tollesbury - Woodrolfe Boatyard, Tollesbury Marina

Tel: (0621) 869202

Type:	concrete slipway into marina
Suits:	all craft
Availability:	approx. 2½ hours either side HW during working hours
Restrictions:	4 knot speed limit in Woodrolfe Ck, 8 knots in Tollesbury Fleet: check for availability before use
Facilities:	diesel on site, parking for car and trailer, toilets, showers, crane, hoist, moorings and other marina facilities on site
Dues:	none
Charge:	yes
Directions:	from Maldon take B1026 to Tolleshunt D'Arcy turning right onto B1023 to Tollesbury: drive through village taking left fork into Woodrolfe Rd

Waters accessed: Woodrolfe Creek, Tollesbury Fleet and River Blackwater

Tollesbury - The Saltings

Tel: (0621) 868624

Type:	concrete slipway
Suits:	small craft
Availability:	approx. 2 hours either side HW by prior arrangement
Restrictions:	speed limit: water-skiing in designated areas in River Blackwater
Facilities:	diesel, parking for car and trailer, toilets on site: chandlery and outboard repairs nearby
Dues:	none
Charge:	approx. £5.00
Directions:	from Maldon take B1026 to Tolleshunt D'Arcy turning right onto B1023 to Tollesbury: drive through village taking left fork into Woodrolfe Rd: site is behind sail lofts by sea wall

Waters accessed: Woodrolfe Creek, Tollesbury Fleet and River Blackwater

Type:	launching over shingle onto soft mud
Suits:	dinghies, sailboards and pwc
Availability:	approx. 2 hours either side HW
Restrictions:	very limited parking on road which floods on spring tides
Facilities:	site is used mainly by pwc, there are no facilities at this site
Dues:	none
Charge:	none
Directions:	from Colchester follow B1025 to Mersea Island: site is on mainland side of causeway on the left hand side of the road

Waters accessed: Pyefleet Channel, River Colne and River Blackwater

---

West Mersea - Public Hard, Coast Road (previously 'Lifeboat Hard')
Tel: (0206) 382244

Type:	wide concrete and shingle hard
Suits:	all craft
Availability:	approx. 3 hours either side HW
Restrictions:	speed limit through moorings: waterskiing permitted in Strood channel above moorings
Facilities:	fuel, limited parking for car and trailer, toilets and chandlery nearby
Dues:	none
Charge:	none
Directions:	from Colchester follow B1025 to Mersea Island and signs to West Mersea: follow road through village to waterfront

Waters accessed: Blackwater Estuary

Rowhedge - Public Hard

Type:	concrete slipway onto mud
Suits:	small dinghies only
Availability:	approx. 1½ hours either side HW
Restrictions:	6 knot speed limit: water-skiing and pwc prohibited: awkward right-angled approach to slipway: site owned by Rowhedge Hard Assn
Facilities:	fuel in village, limited parking for car and trailer in road
Dues:	none
Charge:	none
Directions:	from Colchester follow inner relief road (Southway) east, straight across roundabout by Colchester Town railway station then right fork into Military Road at traffic lights (signposted Rowhedge): continue following this road until left fork to Rowhedge: site is adjacent Anchor Inn

Waters accessed: River Colne and Blackwater Estuaruy

Type:	shingle hard
Suits:	small craft
Availability:	approx. 2½ hours either side HW
Restrictions:	8 knot speed limit; waterskiing and pwc prohibited
Facilities:	no fuel, limited parking for car and trailer
Dues:	none
Charge:	none
Directions:	from Colchester take A133 towards Clacton, turning right onto B1027 and at Alresford turn right into village: follow road past railway station and take road marked 'Ford'

Waters accessed: Alresford Creek, River Colne and Blackwater Estuary

Brightlingsea - Town Hard
Tel: (0206) 302200 (Harbour Office)

Type:	concrete and shingle hard
Suits:	all craft
Availability:	all states of tide
Restrictions:	5 knot speed limit in creek: water-skiing in designated area for members of Brightlingsea Powerboat and Water Ski Club only
Facilities:	fuel, parking for car and trailer in Tower St or Oyster Tank Rd (c), toilets, chandlers and pub all available on site or nearby
Dues:	none
Charge:	yes
Directions:	from Colchester take A133 towards Clacton: turn right onto B1027 to Thorrington cross roads and turn right onto B1029: at Brightlingsea follow signs to Waterfront

Waters accessed: Brightlingsea Creek, River Colne and Blackwater Estuary

St Osyth - St Osyth Boatyard
Tel: (0255) 820005

Type:	concrete slipway
Suits:	dinghies and trailer-sailers
Availability:	approx. 2 hours (max.) either side HW during working hours by prior arrangement
Restrictions:	speed limit in creek: powercraft and pwc prohibited: creek is narrow and use very limited by tide
Facilities:	no fuel, parking for car and trailer nearby, toilets on site
Dues:	none
Charge:	approx. £3.00
Directions:	from Colchester take A133 towards Clacton turning right onto B1027 near Essex University: turn right into St Osyth village turning right again past 'Priory' to creek: site is on right

Waters accessed: St Osyth Creek, River Colne and Blackwater Estuary

St Osyth - Lakeside Inn
Tel: (0255) 820535

Type:	concrete slipway
Suits:	powerboats and pwc only
Availability:	at all times by arrangement only
Restrictions:	site is for water-skiing and pwc only
Facilities:	no fuel, parking for car and trailer, toilets, bar and restaurant
Dues:	none
Charge:	approx. £15 for non members
Directions:	from Colchester take A133 towards Clacton: turn right onto B1027 near Essex University: turn right into St Osyth village and right again past 'Priory' to creek: site is on left at top of creek

Waters accessed: Mill Dam Lake only

St Osyth - Multi Marine and Auto, Point Clear Bay
Tel: (0255) 821561

Type:	concrete slipway
Suits:	all craft up to 18' LOA
Availability:	all states of tide but best approx. 3-4 hours either side HW
Restrictions:	5 knot speed limit: water-skiing not permitted
Facilities:	fuel, parking for car and trailer, toilets
Dues:	none
Charge:	yes
Directions:	from Colchester take A133 towards Clacton: turn right onto B1027 near Essex University: turn right into St Osyth village and right again past 'Priory' and follow signs to Point Clear

Waters accessed: River Colne and Blackwater Estuary

Clacton-on-Sea - Gunfleet Slipway
Tel: (0255) 425501 (Tendring D.C.)

Type:	concrete slipway
Suits:	dinghies and small powered craft only
Availability:	approx. 3 hours either side HW
Restrictions:	8 knot speed limit within 100m of LW mark: water-skiing permitted outside this area: site is at right angles to road and manoeuvring is difficult
Facilities:	fuel, parking for car and trailer (c), toilets
Dues:	none
Charge:	none
Directions:	from Colchester follow A133 to Clacton then signs to seafront: site is opposite Lyndhurst Rd

Waters accessed: Thames Estuary and North Sea

Clacton-on-Sea - Marine Parade West
Tel: (0255) 425501 (Tendring D.C.)

Type:	concrete slipway onto hard sand
Suits:	all craft up to 20' LOA
Availability:	approx. 2½ hours either side HW
Restrictions:	8 knot speed limit within 100m of LW mark: water-skiing permitted outside this area
Facilities:	fuel in town, parking for car (c), toilets
Dues:	none
Charge:	none
Directions:	from Colchester follow A133 to Clacton then signs to seafront: site is to south of Pier

Waters accessed: Thames Estuary and North Sea

Clacton-on-Sea - Holland Haven, Holland-on-Sea
Tel: (0255) 425501 (Tendring D.C.)

Type:	concrete slipway onto sand
Suits:	dinghies only
Availability:	approx. 3 hours either side HW
Restrictions:	8 knot speed limit within 100m of LW mark: water-skiing permitted outside this area
Facilities:	no fuel, parking for car and trailer (c), toilets
Dues:	none
Charge:	yes
Directions:	from Colchester follow A133 to Clacton then B1032 to Holland-on-Sea and signs to seafront: access is from Esplanade and adjacent Clacton-on-Sea SC

Waters accessed: Thames Estuary and North Sea

Frinton-on-Sea - The Esplanade
Tel: (0255) 425501 (Tendring D.C.)

Type:	concrete slipway onto hard sand
Suits:	all craft
Availability:	approx. 3 hours either side HW
Restrictions:	8 knot speed limit inshore: water-skiing permitted outside limit: access is via locked barrier, key from Beach Attendant or Council Offices, Old Rd, Frinton
Facilities:	fuel in town, parking for car and trailer (c) on site and toilets nearby, chandlers in town
Dues:	none
Charge:	yes
Directions:	from Colchester follow A133 and B1033 turning right at station over level crossing and follow signs to seafront:

Waters accessed: Thames Estuary and North Sea

Frinton-on-Sea - The Leas

Type:	concrete slipway onto hard sand
Suits:	all craft up to 20' LOA
Availability:	all states of tide
Restrictions:	8 knot speed limit inshore: water-skiing permitted outside limit
Facilities:	fuel, parking for car and trailer (c), toilets: chandlers in town
Dues:	none
Charge:	none
Directions:	from Colchester follow A133 and B1033 turning right at station over level crossing and follow signs to seafront: site is accessed from Cliff Way
Waters accessed:	Thames Estuary and North Sea

Walton-on-the-Naze - The Beach

Type:	concrete slipway onto hard sand
Suits:	all craft up to 20' LOA
Availability:	approx. 2 hours either side HW
Restrictions:	8 knot speed limit inshore: water-skiing permitted outside limit
Facilities:	fuel in town, parking for car (c) but not for trailer, toilets
Dues:	none
Charge:	yes
Directions:	from Colchester follow A133/B1033: turn left onto B1034 to town centre and follow signs to seafront: site is on N side of Pier
Waters accessed:	Thames Estuary and North Sea

Walton-on-the-Naze - Town Hard

Type:	launching over shingle foreshore
Suits:	all craft up to 20' LOA
Availability:	approx. 1½ hours either side HW
Restrictions:	8 knot speed limit: water-skiing prohibited
Facilities:	fuel, parking for car and trailer(c), toilets and chandlers nearby
Dues:	none
Charge:	none
Directions:	from Colchester follow A133/B1033: turn left onto B1034 after Thorpe-le-Soken and left again off High St into Mill Lane
Waters accessed:	Walton Backwaters and Thames Estuary

Walton-on-theNaze - Titchmarsh Marina, Coles Lane, Kirby Road
Tel: (0255) 672185

Type:	concrete slipway
Suits:	dinghies and small powered craft
Availability:	all states of tide 0800-1700

Restrictions:	speed limit: no speed boats, high powered craft, or sailboards
Facilities:	diesel on site, petrol nearby, parking for car and trailer, toilets, chandlery, outboard repairs, crane, travel lift, rigging service, restaurant and bar all on site
Dues:	none
Charge:	approx. £8.00
Directions:	from Colchester follow A133/B1033: turn left onto B1034 after Thorpe-le-Soken and left at sign at approach to town
Waters accessed:	Walton Backwaters and Thames Estuary

Dovercourt - Seafront

Type:	concrete slipway onto sand
Suits:	all craft
Availability:	approx. 2 hours either side HW
Restrictions:	8 knot speed limit in harbour, water-skiing permitted in designated area clear of shipping channel
Facilities:	fuel in town, parking for car and trailer (c), toilets
Dues:	none
Charge:	yes
Directions:	from Colchester take A1232 towards Ipswich and then A120 east to Harwich: follow signs to Dovercourt and seafront and site is adjacent boating lake
Waters accessed:	Harwich Harbour and Thames Estuary

Harwich - Kings Quay Slip, Wellington Road

Type:	concrete slipway onto shingle
Suits:	all craft
Availability:	all states of tide for small boats, approx. 3 hours either side HW for larger craft
Restrictions:	8 knot speed limit: no water-skiing in harbour: this is a busy commercial harbour and craft must keep clear of deep water channel and ferry terminals
Facilities:	fuel nearby, parking for car and trailer, toilets, chandlery all nearby
Dues:	none
Charge:	none
Directions:	from Colchester take A1232 towards Ipswich and then A120 east to Harwich: site is accessed via Kings Quay St and is adjacent to Harwich Town SC
Waters accessed:	Harwich Harbour and North Sea

Type: fairly steep concrete slipway
Suits: small craft
Availability: approx. 2 hours either side HW
Restrictions: speed limit: water-skiing permitted in designated area downstream
Facilities: fuel nearby, parking for car and trailer in road, toilets nearby
Dues: none
Charge: none
Directions: from Colchester follow A137, turning right at roundabout near Manningtree Railway Station and left at end of High St: site is opposite Stour SC
Waters accessed: River Stour, Harwich Harbour and North Sea

Brantham - Cattawade Street

Type: concrete slipway with rollers and hand winch
Suits: small craft that can be manhandled
Availability: approx. 1½ hours either side HW for launching into tidal river or at all times for launching into non-tidal waterway
Restrictions: speed limit: non-tidal river only suitable for small boats without masts; winch on slipway is locked, key from Sluice Keeper - see notice: no direct vehicular access to slipway
Facilities: fuel nearby, limited parking for car and trailer, pub and restaurant nearby
Dues: none
Charge: none
Directions: from Colchester follow A137 north: after crossing river turn right and right again into Cattawade St; site is to left of old bridge past cottages
Waters accessed: tidal and non-tidal River Stour and Harwich Harbour

Pin Mill - Foreshore

Type: launching over gently sloping shingle foreshore
Suits: small craft only
Availability: approx. 2-3 hours either side HW
Restrictions: 6 knot speed limit: water-skiing in designated area east of Levington Marina; beware commercial traffic in main channel; access road is narrow
Facilities: fuel, parking for car and trailer (c), toilets, chandlery, boatyard facilities nearby, pub
Dues: none
Charge: none
Directions: from Ipswich take A137, turning left at roundabout onto B1456: follow road to Chelmondiston and turn left to Pin Mill; site is opposite end of road
Waters accessed: River Orwell and Harwich Harbour

Woolverstone - Woolverstone Marina
Tel: (0473) 780206

Type:	concrete slipway
Suits:	small craft except pwc: trailer-sailers by prior arrangement only
Availability:	approx. 4 hours either side HW
Restrictions:	6 knot speed limit: water-skiing in designated area downstream but pwc prohibited: contact marina office prior to launching
Facilities:	fuel, parking for car and trailer, toilets, chandlery and outboard repairs, showers, launderette, 'Schooner' club and restaurant
Dues:	none
Charge:	approx. £10.60 craft up to 14' LOA: £16.50 craft over 14' LOA
Directions:	from Ipswich take A137, turning left at roundabout onto B1456: follow road and turn left at sign to Marina before Woolverstone Hall
Waters accessed:	River Orwell and Harwich Harbour

Levington - Suffolk Yacht Harbour
Tel: (0473) 659240

Type:	concrete slipway
Suits:	all craft
Availability:	all states of tide
Restrictions:	6 knot speed limit; pwc prohibited
Facilities:	fuel, parking for car and trailer, toilets, chandlery and outboard repairs all available on site
Dues:	approx. £4.50
Charge:	approx. £8.00
Directions:	from Ipwich take A45 to Felixstowe turning right at sign to Marina
Waters accessed:	River Orwell and Harwich Harbour

Felixstowe - The Dip, Cliff Road
Tel: (0394) 444364

Type:	concrete slipway onto shingle beach
Suits:	all craft
Availability:	approx. 2 hours either side HW
Restrictions:	none except gate in sea wall may be closed in winter
Facilities:	fuel in town, parking for car (c) on site but not for trailer, toilets
Dues:	none
Charge:	none
Directions:	from Ipswich follow A45 going straight on at roundabout at approach to town and again at next roundabout: turn right at 3rd roundabout into Beatrice Avenue and left into High Rd East at next roundabout; site is on right after Brackenbury Fort car park
Waters accessed:	North Sea

Felixstowe Ferry
Tel: (0394) 282173

Type:	launching over shingle foreshore; steep at LW
Suits:	all craft
Availability:	all states of tide; approx. 4 hours either side HW for larger boats
Restrictions:	8 knot speed limit; water-skiing in designated area under control of East Suffolk Water Ski Club: larger craft should contact Felixstowe Ferry Boatyard Tel: (0394) 282173
Facilities:	diesel, limited parking for car and trailer, toilets and chandlery on site, outboard repairs nearby; cafe, sailing club with showers, etc
Dues:	no additional fee charged
Charge:	approx. £8 for craft under 30hp, £12 for craft over 30hp
Directions:	from Ipswich follow A45 going straight on at roundabout at approach to town and again at next roundabout: turn right at 3rd roundabout into Beatrice Avenue and left into High Rd East: follow road across golf course to ferry
Waters accessed:	River Deben and North Sea

Waldringfield - Foreshore

Type:	short narrow concrete slipway with drop onto shingle and broken concrete
Suits:	sailing dinghies
Availability:	approx. 2 hours either side HW
Restrictions:	8 knot speed limit: narrow access road and limited room to manoeuvre trailers etc.
Facilities:	fuel in village, parking for car and trailer nearby through pub car park, toilets nearby, chandlery adjacent
Dues:	none
Charge:	none
Directions:	from Woodbridge follow A12: turn left at roundabout after Martlesham Heath to Brightwell and Waldringfield; site is on west bank of river, in front of Maybush Inn
Waters accessed:	River Deben

Woodbridge - Robertsons Boatyard, Lime Kiln Quay
Tel: (0394) 382305

Type:	concrete slipway
Suits:	all craft
Availability:	approx. 2 hours either side HW during working hours
Restrictions:	8 knot speed limit: water-skiing prohibited: check for availability
Facilities:	diesel on site, petrol in town, limited parking for car and trailer on site but public car park nearby (c), no toilets, chandlery nearby
Dues:	none
Charge:	yes
Directions:	from Ipswich take A12 and follow signs to Woodbridge: follow road

and turn right at sharp left hand bend before traffic lights; turn right over level crossing and immediately right again: boatyard is on left

Waters accessed: River Deben

Orford - Town Quay
Tel: (0394) 450637 (Orford Town Trust)

Type:	concrete slipway with drop at end
Suits:	all craft up to 20' LOA
Availability:	all states of tide: launching licence is required
Restrictions:	5 knot speed limit through moorings: water-skiing permitted in designated area by licence (max. 40 boats pa and 5 casual on any one day) priority given to members of Alde & Ore Water Ski Club: pwc prohibited
Facilities:	diesel on site, parking for car and trailer nearby (c), toilets nearby, chandlery and outboard repairs on site, moorings
Dues:	none
Charge:	approx. £3 per day (£35 pa); powered craft over 15hp - £20 per day (£80 pa)
Directions:	from Ipswich follow A12, turning onto A1152 at roundabout north of Woodbridge and forking right onto B1084 following signs to Orford: site is at end of village street

Waters accessed: River Ore and River Alde

Aldeburgh - Slaughden Quay (R F Upson & Co)
Tel: (0728) 453047

Type:	concrete slipway onto shingle
Suits:	all craft
Availability:	all states of tide during working hours with permission
Restrictions:	speed limit; water-skiing in designated areas
Facilities:	diesel on site, petrol nearby, parking for car and trailer nearby, toilets and chandlery on site: boatyard services on site
Dues:	approx. £3.50, speedboats approx. £6.00
Charge:	no separate fee charged
Directions:	from Ipswich follow A12 north; turn right onto A1094 to Aldeburgh

Waters accessed: River Alde and River Ore

Walberswick - Harbour Slipway

Type:	concrete slipway
Suits:	all craft up to 20' LOA
Availability:	approx. 4 hours either side HW
Restrictions:	4 knot speed limit in harbour: water-skiing permitted above bridge
Facilities:	no fuel, limited parking for car and trailer, pub nearby
Dues:	approx. £3.00
Charge:	no separate fee

Directions: from Ipswich follow A12 north, turning right at Blythburgh signposted Walberswick: site is adjacent to ferry
Waters accessed: River Blyth and North Sea

Southwold - Public Hard, Blackshore
Tel: (0502) 724712 (Harbour Master)

Type: concrete slipway
Suits: all craft
Availability: approx. 4 hours either side HW
Restrictions: 4 knot speed limit in harbour: water-skiing permitted above bridge
Facilities: diesel nearby, limited parking for car and trailer, toilets, chandlery ,
pub and tearooms nearby
Dues: approx. £3.00
Charge: no separate fee charged
Directions: from Ipswich follow A12 north, turning onto A1095 after Blythburgh:
turn right at 'Kings Head' and left at Quay: site is adjacent old
lifeboat shed
Waters accessed: River Blyth and North Sea

Southwold - Boatyard, Chandlery and Tearoom, Blackshore
Tel: (0502) 722593

Type: concrete slipway
Suits: all craft
Availability: approx. 4 hours either side HW
Restrictions: 4 knot speed limit in harbour: water-skiing permitted above bridge
Facilities: diesel, limited parking for car and trailer, toilets nearby, chandlery
and tearooms on site, pub nearby
Dues: approx. £3.00
Charge: no separate fee charged
Directions: from Ipswich follow A12 north, turning onto A1095 after Blythburgh:
turn right at 'Kings Head' and left at Quay; site is in front of chan-
dlery/tearooms
Waters accessed: River Blyth and North Sea

Southwold - Pier
Tel: (0502) 724712 (Harbour Master)

Type: concrete slipway onto sand
Suits: small craft which can be manhandled
Availability: approx. 3 hours either side HW
Restrictions: 8 knot speed limit inshore: water-skiing permitted outside limit; site
can be exposed in easterly winds and is closed from Nov-May by
flood gates
Facilities: fuel in town, parking for car and trailer, toilets and cafe
Dues: none

Charge:	none
Directions:	from Ipswich follow A12 north, turning onto A1095 after Blythburgh: turn left at Pier Avenue Hotel into Pier Ave; site is at end of road to N of Pier
Waters accessed:	North Sea

Oulton Broad - Oswald's Boatyard

Type:	concrete slipway
Suits:	trailer-sailers and small powered craft
Availability:	approx. 2½ hours either side HW during working hours by prior arrangement
Restrictions:	speed limit: water-skiing prohibited; narrow driveway into boatyard
Facilities:	diesel on site, petrol nearby, parking for car and trailer nearby, toilets on site, chandlery and outboard repairs nearby
Dues:	approx. £4.00
Charge:	approx. £3.00
Directions:	from A12 take A1117 to Oulton Broad: boatyard is on N side of bridge almost opposite Barclays Bank
Waters accessed:	Lake Lothing, Inner Harbour and North Sea: Oulton Broad through road bridge and via Mutford Lock

Gorleston-on-Sea - Riverside Road

Type:	concrete slipway
Suits:	trailer-sailers and small powered craft
Availability:	approx. 4 hours either side HW
Restrictions:	speed limit in river; water-skiing prohibited; Gt Yarmouth is a busy commercial harbour and there are strong tides in entrance; launching at this site is not encouraged by the Port Authority
Facilities:	fuel nearby, parking for car and trailer nearby (c), chandlery and outboard repairs nearb
Dues:	approx. £5.00
Charge:	no additional fee
Directions:	from A12 follow signs to Gorleston High St, turning right to Harbour and Riverside Rd
Waters accessed:	North Sea and Norfolk Broads: access to latter restricted for larger craft by (opening) bridge

Hemsby - Beach

Type:	launching over sandy beach
Suits:	light craft which can be manhandled
Availability:	all states of tide
Restrictions:	8 knot speed limit inshore: water-skiing permitted outside limit; site suitable for use in settled conditions only; access and parking can be difficult at peak times

Facilities:	none
Dues:	none
Charge:	none
Directions:	from Gt Yarmouth follow A149 and B1159 north for about 6 miles: turn right to Hemsby and follow track to beach

Waters accessed: North Sea

Winterton-on-Sea - Beach

Type:	launching over sandy foreshore
Suits:	light craft only
Availability:	all states of tide
Restrictions:	8 knot speed limit inshore: water-skiing permitted outside limit; site suitable for use in settled conditions only; access and parking can be difficult at peak times
Facilities:	none
Dues:	none
Charge:	none
Directions:	from Gt Yarmouth follow A149 and B1159 north for about 8 miles: turn right to Winterton and follow signs to beach

Waters accessed: North Sea

Whimpwell Green - Cart Gap, Eccles Beach

Type:	wooden ramp onto soft sand
Suits:	small craft only
Availability:	approx. 2 hours either side HW
Restrictions:	8 knot speed limit inshore: water-skiing permitted outside limit; conditions can be dangerous here
Facilities:	no fuel, parking for car and trailer, no toilets
Dues:	none
Charge:	none
Directions:	from Gt Yarmouth follow A149 north, then turn right onto B1151 and left onto B1159: follow signs to beach

Waters accessed: North Sea

Happisburgh - Beach

Type:	wooden ramp onto beach
Suits:	small craft only
Availability:	approx. 2 hours either side HW
Restrictions:	8 knot speed limit inshore: water-skiing permitted outside limit; conditions can be dangerous here;
Facilities:	no fuel, limited parking for car and trailer, no toilets
Dues:	none
Charge:	none
Directions:	from Gt Yarmouth follow A149 north, then turn right onto B1151

and left onto B1159; turn off close to Lighthouse
Waters accessed: North Sea

Walcott Gap - Beach

Type:	concrete slipway onto sand
Suits:	light craft only
Availability:	approx. 2 hours either side HW
Restrictions:	8 knot speed limit inshore: water-skiing permitted outside limit; open sea conditions
Facilities:	fuel, parking for car and trailer, toilets
Dues:	none
Charge:	none
Directions:	from Gt Yarmouth follow A149 north, then turn right onto B1150 in N. Walsham and left onto B1159: site is opposite Walcott Caravan Park

Waters accessed: North Sea

Bacton - Beach

Type:	launching over sandy foreshore
Suits:	light craft only
Availability:	approx. 2 hours either side HW
Restrictions:	8 knot speed limit inshore: water-skiing permitted outside limit; site suitable for use in settled conditions only
Facilities:	parking for car and trailer (200yds), no other facilities
Dues:	none
Charge:	none
Directions:	from Gt Yarmouth follow A149 north, then turn right onto B1150 in N. Walsham to coast: follow signs to beach

Waters accessed: North Sea

Mundesley - Beach

Type:	launching over sandy beach with ramps from road
Suits:	light craft only
Availability:	all states of tide
Restrictions:	8 knot speed limit inshore: water-skiing permitted outside limit; site suitable for use in settled conditions only; access and parking can be difficult
Facilities:	none
Dues:	none
Charge:	none
Directions:	from Gt Yarmouth follow A149 north, then turn right onto B1145 in N. Walsham

Waters accessed: North Sea

Overstrand - Beach

Type:	launching over sandy foreshore
Suits:	light craft only
Availability:	all states of tide
Restrictions:	8 knot speed limit inshore: water-skiing permitted outside limit; site suitable for use in settled conditions only
Facilities:	none
Dues:	none
Charge:	none
Directions:	from Cromer take B1159 south east and follow signs to beach
Waters accessed:	North Sea

Cromer

Type:	ramp onto beach
Suits:	small craft which can be manhandled onto ramp
Availability:	all states of tide
Restrictions:	8 knot speed limit inshore: water-skiing permitted outside limit; site suitable for use in settled conditions only; access and parking can be difficult at peak times
Facilities:	fuel from local garages, very limited parking
Dues:	none
Charge:	none
Directions:	from Norwich take A140 north: site is adjacent old lifeboat station
Waters accessed:	North Sea

Cromer - East Runton Gap

Type:	steep concrete slipway onto shingle
Suits:	all craft
Availability:	approx. 2 hours either side HW
Restrictions:	8 knot speed limit inshore: water-skiing permitted outside limit; site used by local fishing boats which may block access
Facilities:	no fuel, parking for car and trailer, toilets
Dues:	none
Charge:	none
Directions:	from Cromer take A149 north west for approx. 3 miles, turning off towards beach: site is close to Gap Caravan Park
Waters accessed:	North Sea

Cromer - West Runton

Type:	ramp onto sandy beach
Suits:	light craft only
Availability:	all states of tide

Restrictions: 8 knot speed limit inshore: water-skiing permitted outside limit; site suitable for use in settled conditions only

Facilities: fuel nearby, parking for car and trailer

Dues: none

Charge: none

Directions: from Cromer take A149 north west turning right onto road to foreshore which ends at ramp

Waters accessed: North Sea

Blakeney - Blakeney Harbour Quay

Type: three concrete slipways

Suits: all craft

Availability: approx. 3 hours either side HW

Restrictions: 8 knot speed limit; water-skiing permitted at west end of harbour;

Facilities: fuel, parking for car and trailer (c), toilets, chandlery and boatyard facilities nearby

Dues: none

Charge: none

Directions: from Cromer follow A149 to Blakeney and then signs to Quay

Waters accessed: North Sea

Blakeney - Morston

Type: launching over shingle foreshore

Suits: all craft

Availability: approx. 3 hours either side HW

Restrictions: 8 knot speed limit; water-skiing permitted at west end of harbour;

Facilities: no fuel, parking for car and trailer, toilets, chandlery and boatyard facilities nearby in village

Dues: none

Charge: none

Directions: from Cromer follow A149 north west and then yellow sign to Quay west of Blakeney

Waters accessed: North Sea

Wells-next-the-Sea - East Quay

Type: concrete slipway with winch and trolley

Suits: all craft up to 16' LOA

Availability: approx. 3 hours either side HW

Restrictions: 5 knot speed limit: water-skiing permitted outside harbour

Facilities: fuel, parking for car and trailer (c), toilets, chandlery nearby

Dues: yes

Charge: no additional fee

Directions: from Cromer take A149 north west, turning off and following signs to harbour

Waters accessed: North Sea

Wells-next-the-Sea - Beach Road

Type:	launching over shingle foreshore
Suits:	dinghies
Availability:	approx. 3 hours either side HW
Restrictions:	none known
Facilities:	fuel, parking for car and trailer (c), toilets, chandlery nearby
Dues:	yes
Charge:	none
Directions:	from Cromer take A149 north west, turning off and following signs to harbour: Beach Rd is opposite the caravan site

Waters accessed: North Sea

Burnham Overy Staithe
Tel: (0328) 738348 (Burnham Overy Boathouse)

Type:	steep concrete slipway onto shingle
Suits:	dinghies
Availability:	approx. 2 hours either side HW
Restrictions:	8 knot speed limit: powerboats prohibited; site can be very congested at peak times
Facilities:	petrol nearby, no diesel, parking for car nearby but not for trailer, no toilets, chandlery and outboard repairs on site
Dues:	approx. £7.00
Charge:	no additional fee
Directions:	from Hunstanton follow A149 east for approx. 12 miles: site is opposite Burnham Overy Boathouse

Waters accessed: The Wash and North Sea

Brancaster Harbour - The Beach

Type:	launching over shingle (several sites in harbour)
Suits:	small boats
Availability:	approx. 2-3 hours either side HW
Restrictions:	6 knot speed limit in harbour: water-skiing allowed outside limits; Harbour Master's permission needed to launch powerboats and sailboarding is restricted
Facilities:	fuel, parking for car and trailer (c), toilets, chandlery nearby
Dues:	none
Charge:	yes
Directions:	from Hunstanton follow A149 east, turning off to follow signs

Waters accessed: The Wash and North Sea

Hunstanton - North Beach
Tel: (0485) 532610 (Seafront Manager)

Type:	concrete slipway onto hard sand
Suits	sailing dinghies and sailboards only
Availability:	all states of tide but best approx. 2-3 hours either side HW
Restrictions:	7 knot speed limit within 200m HW mark: powered craft prohibited
Facilities:	fuel, parking for car and trailer (c), toilets
Dues:	none
Charge:	none
Directions:	turn off A149: site is adjacent Pier and SC
Waters accessed:	The Wash and North Sea

Hunstanton - South Beach Road (Hunstanton Water Sports Club)
Tel: (0485) 535827 (cafe) or (0485) 535940 (clubhouse)

Type:	concrete slipway onto hard sand
Suits	powercraft and pwc only
Availability:	approx. 3 hours either side HW 0900-1800
Restrictions:	certificate of 3rd party insurance required
Facilities:	fuel nearby, parking for car and trailer (c), toilets, outboard repairs, cafe, showers, licensed bar on site; changing rooms on site for club members only
Dues:	none
Charge:	approx. £10.00
Directions:	from Kings Lynn take A149 north to Hunstanton; at 1st roundabout turn left and head for coast
Waters accessed:	The Wash and North Sea

Hunstanton - Heacham Beach North
Tel: (0485) 532610 (Seafront Manager)

Type:	launching over sand with tractor assistance
Suits	all craft up to 20' LOA
Availability:	approx. 2-3 hours either side HW
Restrictions:	speed limit; water-skiing permitted outside limit; all craft must show insurance certificate before launching
Facilities:	no fuel, parking for car and trailer (c), boat park (c), toilets
Dues:	none
Charge:	none
Directions:	from Kings Lynn take A149 north: turn off and follow signs
Waters accessed:	The Wash and North Sea

Kings Lynn - Common Staithe Quay

Type:	concrete slipway
Suits:	all craft
Availability:	approx. 2 hours either side HW
Restrictions:	at LW thick mud is exposed
Facilities:	fuel, parking for car and trailer (c), toilets on site, chandlery nearby
Dues:	none
Charge:	none
Directions:	follow A10 north to Kings Lynn or A47 north west from Norwich
Waters accessed:	River Great Ouse and The Wash

NORFOLK BROADS

Beccles - Beccles Yacht Station
Tel: (0502) 712225

Type:	concrete slipway
Suits:	all craft up to 20' LOA
Availability:	approx. 3 hours either side HW
Restrictions:	speed limit
Facilities:	parking for car and trailer nearby, toilets, crane
Dues:	Broads Authority licence required
Charge:	none
Directions:	follow A146 Beccles bypass and signs to Quay
Waters accessed:	River Waveney

Beccles - Aston Boats, Bridge Wharf
Tel: (0502) 713960

Type:	concrete slipway
Suits:	all craft
Availability:	approx. 4 hours either side HW 0800-1800 mon-fri, sat by prior arrangement
Restrictions:	speed limit: pwc prohibited, water-skiing in designated areas
Facilities:	diesel, parking for car and trailer (c), toilets, outboard repairs near-by
Dues:	Broads Authority licence required
Charge:	approx. £6.00
Directions:	from town centre take old road to Norwich, cross over river: site is down drive 200yds on right
Waters accessed:	River Waveney

Beccles - H E Hipperson, Gillingham Dam
Tel: (0502) 712166

Type:	concrete slipway
Suits:	all craft except deep draught trailer-sailers
Availability:	approx. 4 hours either side HW by prior arrangement only
Restrictions:	speed limit: water-skiing in designated areas with special licence
Facilities:	diesel on site, petrol from local garage, parking for car and trailer (c), toilets on site, outboard repairs nearby; caravan club site
Dues:	Broads Authority licence required
Charge:	approx. £4.00
Directions:	from Norwich follow A146 south east to outskirts of Beccles; at roundabout take 2nd exit signposted Beccles after 400yds turn right through Gillingham: site is on left before river bridge
Waters accessed:	River Waveney

Beccles - Waveney Valley Boats, Puddingmoor
Tel: (0502) 712538

Type:	concrete slipway
Suits:	dinghies and small powered craft up to 20' LOA
Availability:	all states of tide 0900-1700 weekdays, 1100-1700 weekends by prior arrangement only
Restrictions:	5 knot speed limit, pwc and water-skiing prohibited
Facilities:	diesel on site, petrol in town, parking for car and trailer, toilets, outboard repairs, chandlery and crane all on site
Dues:	Broads Authority licence required
Charge:	approx. £12; £30 if assisted by yard
Directions:	from Bungay take A144 and turn left onto B1062; at approach to town turn left into Puddingmoor: site is on left at town end of road
Waters accessed:	River Waveney

Brundall - Brundall Bay Marina, Riverside Estate
Tel (0603) 716606

Type:	concrete slipway
Suits:	all craft
Availability:	0830-1730 daily
Restrictions:	speed limit: ski boats prohibited from site
Facilities:	diesel on site, petrol nearby, parking for car (c) and trailer (c) by arrangement, toilets, outboard repairs on site, chandlery nearby
Dues:	Broads Authority licence required
Charge:	approx. £5.00
Directions:	from Norwich take A47 east towards Gt Yarmouth; at 1st roundabout take last exit signposted Brundall and turn right at Barclays Bank
Waters accessed:	River Yare

Brundall - Bell Boats Ltd
Tel: (0603) 713109

Type:	launching by crane only
Suits:	larger craft up to 35 tons
Availability:	all states of tide during working hours
Restrictions:	speed limit
Facilities:	fuel, moorings, storage, boat repairs and servicing
Dues:	Broads Authority licence required
Charge:	approx. £42 craft up to 23'LOA, thereafter at £1 76 per foot
Directions:	from Norwich take A47 east towards Gt Yarmouth; at 1st round-about take last exit signposted Brundall

Waters accessed: River Yare

Brundall - Harbour Cruisers, Riverside Estate
Tel: (0603) 712146

Type:	concrete slipway
Suits:	all craft
Availability:	all states of tide during working hours
Restrictions:	speed limit: pwc prohibited; water-skiing in designated area at certain times with special licence
Facilities:	diesel on site, petrol nearby, parking for car and trailer (c), toilets on site, chandlery nearby
Dues:	Broads Authority licence required
Charge:	approx. £4.00
Directions:	from Norwich take A47 east towards Gt Yarmouth; at 1st round-about take last exit signposted Brundall and turn right after 1 mile into Station Rd; site is half a mile on left

Waters accessed: River Yare

Buckenham Ferry - Paul Wright Mouldings Ltd
Tel: (0508) 480218

Type:	concrete slipway
Suits:	all craft up to 25' LOA
Availability:	all states of tide during working hours
Restrictions:	speed limit: water-skiing permitted in designated areas with special licence
Facilities:	no fuel, parking for car and trailer nearby (c), toilets nearby, fibreglass repairs on site, pub and restaurant adjacent to site
Dues:	Broads Authority licence required
Charge:	approx. £2.00
Directions:	from Norwich take A146, turning left at sign to Kirby Bedon, Rockland and Claxton: go through Claxton and after ½ mile look for sign to left to boatyard and river

Waters accessed: River Yare

Burgh Castle - Burgh Castle Marina
Tel: (0493) 780331

Type:	concrete slipway
Suits:	all craft
Availability:	approx. 4 hours either side HW by prior arrangement to obtain weekly ticket and key to barrier
Restrictions:	water-skiing permitted with special licence
Facilities:	diesel nearby, parking for car and trailer, toilets, chandlery, caravan site, sales and camping and marina facilities all on site
Dues:	Broads Authority licence required
Charge:	approx. £20.00
Directions:	from Gt Yarmouth take A143 west following signs to Burgh Castle
Waters accessed:	River Waveney

Burgh Castle - Goodchild Marine Services, Burgh Castle Yacht Station
Tel: (0493) 782301

Type:	launching by travel hoist; concrete slipway normally in use
Suits:	all craft
Availability:	all states of tide 0800-1800 by prior arrangement
Restrictions:	no speed limit on Breydon Water:water-skiing permitted with special licence
Facilities:	diesel, parking for car and trailer, toilets, chandlery, outboard repairs, rigging, pump-out and full boatyard services
Dues:	Broads Authority licence required
Charge:	approx. £24.00
Directions:	from Gt Yarmouth take A143 west, approx. 2 miles after Gorleston roundabout turn right following signs to Burgh Castle and Belton: site entrance is ½ mile S of village
Waters accessed:	River Waveney and Breydon Water

Burgh St Peter - Waveney River Centre
Tel: (0502) 677217/677343

Type:	concrete slipway
Suits:	dinghies and powered craft
Availability:	approx. 3-4 hours either side HW
Restrictions:	speed limit, no water-skiing except in designated areas with special licence
Facilities:	fuel, parking for car and trailer (c), toilets and showers, pub. crane, shop and caravan site
Dues:	Broads Authority licence required
Charge:	approx. £3
Directions:	from Gt Yarmouth take A143 towards Beccles after Haddiscoe turn left onto minor roads and follow signs
Waters accessed:	River Waveney

Hickling - Whispering Reeds Boats Ltd, Staithe Road
Tel: (0692) 598314

Type:	concrete slipway
Suits:	dinghies, trailer-sailers, windsurfers and small powered craft
Availability:	0730-1700 mon-fri.,0800-1700 sat; Easter to end Oct 0900-1700 sun
Restrictions:	speed limit: water-skiing prohibited
Facilities:	fuel at Martham, parking for car and trailer, (c) for trailer if left more than 1 day, toilets, shower: Hickling is a well known nature reserve
Dues:	Broads Authority licence required
Charge:	approx. £5.50
Directions:	from Norwich take A1151 through Wroxham; at junction with A149 turn right through Stalham and after approx. 2½ miles turn left to Hickling; at 'T' junction turn left and at next cross roads right; site is past Pleasure Boat Inn

Waters accessed: Hickling Broad

Horning - next The Swan Inn, The Street

Type:	concrete slipway
Suits:	small craft
Availability:	at all times
Restrictions:	speed limit: water-skiing prohibited; access is via locked barrier, key from The Paper Shop
Facilities:	fuel in village, limited parking for car and trailer, toilets nearby
Dues:	Broads Authority licence required
Charge:	yes
Directions:	from Norwich take A1151 to Wroxham, turning right onto A1062 and right again into Horning village

Waters accessed: River Bure

Horning - Horning Pleasurecraft Ltd
Tel: (0692) 630366

Type:	launching by travel hoist only
Suits:	larger craft up to 6 tons and 3' draught
Availability:	0900-1800 daily
Restrictions:	speed limit: water-skiing prohibited; there is a hire fleet here so launching may be restricted at weekends
Facilities:	fuel, parking for car and trailer (c), toilets and boatyard facilities
Dues:	Broads Authority licence required
Charge:	yes
Directions:	from Norwich take A1151 to Wroxham, turning right onto A1062 and right again into Horning village: site is down gravel lane on right at far end of village

Waters accessed: River Bure

Horning - Woodsdyke Boatyard, Ferry Road
Tel: (0692) 630461

Type:	launching by crane only
Suits:	larger craft only
Availability:	at all times by prior arrangement
Restrictions:	speed limit, no water-skiing;
Facilities:	fuel in village, parking for car and trailer (c), toilets
Dues:	Broads Authority licence required
Charge:	approx.£2 per foot
Directions:	from Norwich take A1151 to Wroxham, turning right onto A1062 and right again into Horning village: site is at far end of village
Waters accessed:	River Bure

Loddon - Greenway Marine, Riverside
Tel: (0508) 520397

Type:	launching by boatlift only
Suits:	larger craft under 11' height on trailer
Availability:	all states of tide during normal working hours by prior arrangement
Restrictions:	speed limit: water-skiing permitted at certain times with special licence
Facilities:	diesel on site, parking for car and trailer, toilet, pump-out
Dues:	Broads Authority licence required
Charge:	approx. £35 per lift craft up to 22' LOA, plus £1.60 per ft over 22' LOA
Directions:	from Norwich take A146 towards Beccles turning off into Loddon Village; yard is down track opposite service station
Waters accessed:	River Chet

Ludham Bridge - Ludham Bridge Services, Johnsons Street
Tel: (0692) 630486/630322

Type:	launching by crane
Suits:	all craft up to 5 tons
Availability:	at all times during working hours
Restrictions:	speed limit; pwc and water-skiing prohibited
Facilities:	fuel, parking for car on site and for trailer nearby (c), toilets (100yds), chandlery, outboard repairs, gas, towing and hire of boats and outboards all on site
Dues:	Broads Authority licence required
Charge:	yes
Directions:	from Norwich take A1151 to Wroxham, turn right onto A1062 to Ludham Bridge
Waters accessed:	River Ant

Martham - Martham Boat Building Co, Riverside, Cess Road
Tel: (0493) 740249

Type:	concrete slipway
Suits:	dinghies, trailer-sailers and small powered craft
Availability:	0800-1630 by prior arrangement
Restrictions:	speed limit: water-skiing prohibited; locked barrier
Facilities:	fuel, parking for car and trailer (c), toilets, pump-out, showers
Dues:	Broads Authority licence required
Charge:	approx. £9.00
Directions:	from Gt Yarmouth take A149 north; turn right onto B1152 to Martham
Waters accessed:	River Thurne

Oulton Broad - Watersports Centre, North Bay
Tel: (0502) 574946 (Harbour Master)

Type:	two concrete slipways
Suits:	all craft
Availability:	approx. 3 hours either side HW
Restrictions:	6 knot speed limit: water-skiing prohibited
Facilities:	fuel, parking for car and trailer, toilets, chandlery nearby
Dues:	Broads Authority licence required
Charge:	none
Directions:	from Lowestoft follow A146; site is south of road bridge
Waters accessed:	Oulton Broad

Oulton Broad - Wherry Hotel
Tel: (0502) 573521

Type:	concrete slipway
Suits:	small craft
Availability:	at all times by arrangement with hotel
Restrictions:	speed limit; water-skiing prohibited
Facilities:	fuel nearby, parking for car and trailer (c), chandlery nearby, toilets
Dues:	Broads Authority licence required
Charge:	yes
Directions:	take A146 towards Beccles: hotel is on north side of bridge
Waters accessed:	Oulton Broad

Oulton Broad - Colmans Land Slipway, Bridge Road

Type:	concrete slipway
Suits:	small craft
Availability:	at all times
Restrictions:	speed limit: water-skiing prohibited
Facilities:	fuel, parking for car and trailer (c), toilets and chandlers nearby

Dues:	Broads Authority licence required
Charge:	no
Directions:	from Lowestoft take A146 towards Beccles: site is south of bridge and Nicholas Everitt Park on right
Waters accessed:	Oulton Broad

Reedham Ferry - Reedham Ferry Inn
Tel: (0493) 700429 (Mr Archer)

Type:	concrete slipway with good slope
Suits:	craft up to 30' LOA
Availability:	0800-2200 by prior arrangement
Restrictions:	speed limit: water-skiing prohibited; keep clear of chain ferry and beware of deceptive tidal flow; private slipway, permission of owner always required
Facilities:	no fuel, parking for car and trailer (c), toilets, pub
Dues:	Broads Authority licence required
Charge:	approx. £4.00 incl parking
Directions:	from Norwich take A47 towards Gt Yarmouth; turn right onto B1140 south at Damgate
Waters accessed:	River Yare

Repps - Repps Staithe

Type:	concrete slipway
Suits:	craft up to 16' LOA
Availability:	all states of tide
Restrictions:	speed limit
Facilities:	no fuel, limited parking for car and trailer (c)
Dues:	licence required
Charge:	no
Directions:	take A149 north, turning left onto minor road to Repps
Waters accessed:	River Thurne

St Olaves - next Bridge
Tel: (0493) 488230 (Bridge Stores - Mrs Miller)

Type:	concrete slipway
Suits:	small craft only
Availability:	at all times by prior arrangement
Restrictions:	speed limit: locked access, obtain key from Bridge Stores
Facilities:	fuel and parking for car and trailer nearby
Dues:	Broads Authority licence required
Charge:	approx. £3.00
Directions:	from Gt Yarmouth take A143 towards Beccles: site is by bridge opposite Bell Inn
Waters accessed:	River Waveney

Stalham - Richardsons (Stalham) Ltd
Tel: (0692) 581081

Type:	concrete slipway
Suits:	dinghies, trailer-sailers and small powered craft up to 40' LOA
Availability:	all times during working hours mon- fri, 0900-1230 on sun
Restrictions:	speed limit: water-skiing prohibited
Facilities:	diesel on site, parking for car and trailer (c), toilets, diving supplies nearby, crane, repairs and overhauls on site
Dues:	Broads Authority licence required
Charge:	approx. £10
Directions:	from Norwich take A1151 and turn left onto A149 to Stalham
Waters accessed:	River Ant

Stalham - Stalham Yacht Services
Tel: (0692) 580288

Type:	concrete slipway
Suits:	dinghies, trailer-sailers and small powered craft
Availability:	at all times during normal working hours mon- fri and sun
Restrictions:	speed limit: water-skiing prohibited
Facilities:	diesel, parking for car and trailer (c), toilets, crane and boatyard
Dues:	Broads Authority licence required
Charge:	approx. £16
Directions:	from Norwich take A1151 and turn left onto A149 to Stalham
Waters accessed:	River Ant

Thorpe - Griffin Marine, Griffin Lane
Tel: (0603) 33253

Type:	concrete slipway into 4' water
Suits:	all craft
Availability:	at all times
Restrictions:	speed limit; pwc prohibited; water-skiing permitted in designated area with special licence
Facilities:	diesel on site, petrol nearby, parking for car and trailer (c), toilets, chandlery, outboard repairs, fishing tackle and bait all on site, diving supplies nearby; breakdown service available (24 hrs)
Dues:	Broads Authority licence required
Charge:	approx. £4.00
Directions:	from Norwich take A47 towards Gt Yarmouth; site is off this road on outskirts of city
Waters accessed:	River Yare

Wroxham - Landamores Boatyard, Marsh Rd, Hoveton
Tel: (0603) 782212

Type:	concrete slipway
Suits:	all craft with up to 2' draught on trailer
Availability:	at all times 0800-1730 mon- fri by prior arrangement
Restrictions:	speed limit: access may be restricted by parked cars
Facilities:	fuel nearby, parking for car and trailer (c), toilets, chandlery, crane and boatyard facilities on site on site, outboard repairs nearby
Dues:	Broads Authority licence required
Charge:	approx. £4.00
Directions:	from Norwich take A1151 turn right at cross roads after Wroxham Bridge into Church Rd and right again into Marsh Rd (200yds)
Waters accessed:	River Bure

Wroxham - Moore & Co, Staitheway Road
Tel: (0603) 783311

Type:	concrete slipway
Suits:	all craft up to 35' LOA
Availability:	at all times except sun pm
Restrictions:	speed limit: access to site is via locked barrier
Facilities:	diesel on site, petrol nearby, parking for car and trailer (c), toilets on site, chandlery, outboard repairs and diving supplies nearby
Dues:	Broads Authority licence required
Charge:	approx. £7.50
Directions:	from Norwich take A1151 to Wroxham; turn right down avenues and 1st left into Staitheway Rd; site is at end of road
Waters accessed:	River Bure

LAKE SITES

Milton Keynes - Willen Watersports, Willen Lake, Brickhill Street
Tel: (0908) 670197

Type:	concrete slipway
Suits:sailing	dinghies, windsurfers and canoes
Availability:	0900 - 1 hour before lighting up time
Restrictions:	powered craft prohibited
Facilities:	parking for car and trailer, toilets, hotel and bar facilities
Dues:	none
Charge:	approx.£8.00 mon -fri, £10.00 weekends
Directions:	from M1: leave at junction 14 take A509 west for approx. 2 miles
Waters accessed:	Willen Lake

Wyboston, Bedfordshire - Wyboston Watersports Centre
Tel: (0480) 213100

Type:	two concrete slipways into 5' water
Suits:	powered craft up to 19' LOA
Availability:	Mar-Oct 0900-dusk, winter opening by prior arrangement only
Restrictions:	no sailing craft: proof of insurance required
Facilities:	fuel nearby, parking for car and trailer, toilets and clubhouse facilities on site, chandlery and outboard repairs nearby
Dues:	none
Charge:	approx. £10.00 per hour weekdays, weekends £30 - ½ day or £50 - day
Directions:	from A1 take A428(A45) east towards Cambridge and follow signs
Waters accessed:	Wyboston Water

Grafham Water - Grafham Water SC
Tel: (0480) 810478

Type:	concrete slipway
Suits:	sailing dinghies, trailer-sailers and windsurfers
Availability:	0930-1 hour before sunset
Restrictions:	no powered craft
Facilities:	parking for car and trailer, toilets, chandlery, windsurfing shop and RYA courses in windsurfing, dinghy and catamaran sailing
Dues:	none
Charge:	approx.£3.50 per craft plus £3.50 per person weekdays; £6.00 per craft and £6.00 per person sun
Directions:	from A1 take B661 at Buckden roundabout, continue for approx. 2 miles to village of Perry and turn right opposite ' Wheatsheaf' pub: site is at end of road
Waters accessed:	Grafham Water

North East Coast:
Boston to Berwick upon Tweed

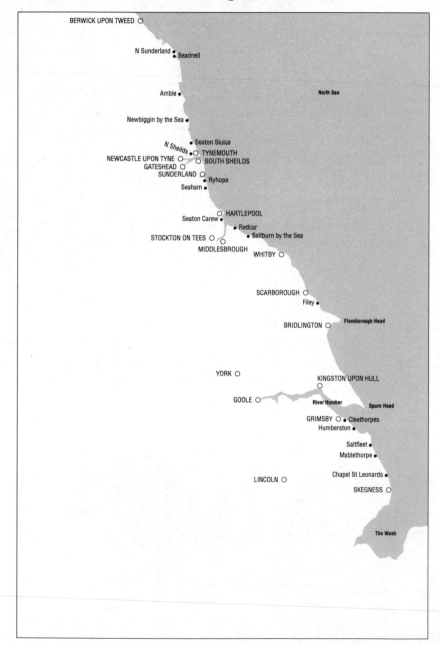

BERWICK UPON TWEED ○

N Sunderland ● ● Beadnell

Amble ●

North Sea

Newbiggin by the Sea ●

● Seaton Sluice
N Sheilds ●
○ TYNEMOUTH
NEWCASTLE UPON TYNE ○ ○ SOUTH SHEILDS
GATESHEAD ○
SUNDERLAND ○
● Ryhope
Seaham ●

○ HARTLEPOOL
Seaton Carew ●
● Redcar
STOCKTON ON TEES ○ ○ ● Saltburn by the Sea
MIDDLESBROUGH
WHITBY ○

SCARBOROUGH ○
Filey ●

BRIDLINGTON ○ ● Flamborough Head

YORK ○

KINGSTON UPON HULL
○
GOOLE ○
River Humber   Spurn Head
GRIMSBY ○ ● Cleethorpes
Humberston ●

Saltfleet ●
Mablethorpe ●

Chapel St Leonards ●
LINCOLN ○
SKEGNESS ○

The Wash

Skegness - Princes Parade
Tel: (0754) 880085 (A. Dingle - Sec: Skegness Boating Club)

Type:	launching over sand
Suits:	craft up to 20' LOA
Availability:	all states of tide with prior permission
Restrictions:	site is controlled by Skegness Boating Club: launching is with assistance of tractor
Facilities:	fuel and toilets nearby
Dues:	none
Charge:	yes
Directions:	follow A158 east from Lincoln
Waters accessed:	The Wash

Skegness - Gibraltar Point
Tel: (0754) 610616 (J. Lee - Sec: Skegness Yacht Club)

Type:	concrete slipway
Suits:	dinghies and trailer-sailers
Availability:	approx. 1 hour either side HW with prior permission
Restrictions	4 knot speed limit; powercraft and pwc prohibited; site is controlled by Skegness YC: contact Secretary
Facilities:	toilets and parking for car and trailer in nearby nature reserve car park (c)
Dues:	none
Charge:	approx. £2.00
Directions:	follow A158 east from Lincoln and minor road 3 miles south from town centre: site is at entrance to Wainfleet Ck
Waters accessed:	The Wash

Skegness - Jacksons Corner, Ingoldmells
Tel: (0533) 374635 (Skegness and District Watersports Centre)

Type:	steep slipway
Suits:	all craft up to 26' LOA: tractor assistance available
Availability:	all states of tide with prior permission
Restrictions:	site is controlled by Skegness and District Watersports Ass'n: contact Secretary; all boats launched must have insurance
Facilities:	fuel nearby, parking for car and trailer, toilets, pub, changing rooms and locked boat compound
Dues:	none
Charge:	approx. £10 incl tractor tow
Directions:	follow A52 north from Skegness to Mablethorpe, turning at side of Butlin's Funcoast Camp and following signs to sea
Waters accessed:	North Sea

Chapel St Leonards - Beach

Type:	pullover onto sand to north of village
Suits:	light craft which can be manhandled; tractor assistance available from local fisherman
Availability:	all states of tide
Restrictions:	not known
Facilities:	parking for car and trailer (c), toilets
Dues:	none
Charge:	none, but may be charge for tractor
Directions:	follow A52 and minor roads approx 6 miles north from Skegness
Waters accessed:	North Sea

Sandilands - Sea Lane Pullover

Type:	pullover onto sandy beach
Suits:	light craft which can be manhandled; tractor assistance available from local fishermen
Availability:	all states of tide
Restrictions:	none
Facilities:	parking for car and trailer (c), toilets, water-skiing and pwc permitted
Dues:	none
Charge:	none, but may be charge for tractor
Directions:	follow A52 and minor roads north from Skegness
Waters accessed:	North Sea

Sutton-on-Sea - Church Lane Pullover

Type:	pullover onto sandy beach
Suits:	light craft which can be manhandled
Availability:	all states of tide
Restrictions:	none
Facilities:	parking for car and trailer in village (¼ mile), toilets and cafe on site; pubs approx. 200yds
Dues:	none
Charge:	none
Directions:	follow A52 north from Skegness
Waters accessed:	North Sea

Mablethorpe - Seaholme Road Pullover

Type:	pullover onto sandy beach
Suits:	light craft which can be manhandled
Availability:	all states of tide
Restrictions:	water-skiing and pwc prohibited
Facilities:	parking for car and trailer (c), toilets, cafe and pub on site

Dues:	none
Charge:	none
Directions:	follow A52 north from Skegness
Waters accessed:	North Sea

Saltfleet - Saltfleet Haven

Type:	stone slipway
Suits:	craft up to 25' LOA
Availability:	approx. 2 hours either side HW
Restrictions:	bar with narrow gap at entrance to Haven; site is dangerous in onshore winds and is controlled by Saltfleet Haven Boat Club: contact Secretary; water-skiing prohibited in Haven
Facilities:	parking for car and trailer, no toilets
Dues:	none
Charge:	yes
Directions:	follow A1031 south from Cleethorpes
Waters accessed:	North Sea

Humberston - Humber Mouth Yacht Club
Tel: (0472) 812063 or 822862 (Mrs Rawcliffe - YC Secretary)

Type:	concrete slipway
Suits:	dinghies and small trailer-sailers
Availability:	approx. 1½ hours either side HW with prior permission
Restrictions:	8 knot speed limit inshore: water-skiing permitted outside limit
Facilities:	no fuel, parking for car and trailer (c) on site, toilets, tractor assistance available, clubhouse for use of members of RYA affiliated clubs, shops (in season) in nearby caravan park
Dues:	none
Charge:	none, but may be for tractor assistance
Directions:	follow A46 and A1031 from Lincoln: site is at end of metalled track through caravan park
Waters accessed:	Tetney Haven, Humber Estuary and North Sea

Cleethorpes - Beach
Tel: (0472) 698828 (First-Aid station) or (0472) 200220 (Information Centre)

Type:	concrete slipway onto shingle
Suits:	small craft
Availability:	approx. 2 hours either side HW
Restrictions:	8 knot speed limit within 200m of shore: water-skiing in designated area with access channel
Facilities:	fuel nearby, parking for car and trailer (c), toilets, chandlery
Dues:	none
Charge:	none
Directions:	follow A46 from Lincoln or M180/A180: site is next to Pier at end of

Sea Road
Waters accessed: Humber Estuary and North Sea

Cleethorpes - Brighton Street Slipway
Tel: (0472) 698828 (First-Aid station) or (0472) 200220 (Information Centre)

Type:	cobbles and concrete slipway
Suits:	small craft which can be manhandled
Availability:	approx. 2 hours either side HW
Restrictions:	8 knot speed limit within 200m of shore: water-skiing in designated area with access channel
Facilities:	fuel, parking for car and trailer (c) and toilets nearby, chandlery
Dues:	none
Charge:	none
Directions:	follow A46 from Lincoln or M180/A180: site is on seafront opposite Brighton Street

Waters accessed: Humber Estuary and North Sea

Goole - Smith Bros (Goole) Ltd Marina
Tel: (0405) 763985

Type:	concrete slipway
Suits:	craft up to 36' LOA and 11'6" wide
Availability:	during working hours or by prior arrangement if assistance required
Restrictions:	check for availability
Facilities:	diesel, parking for car and trailer(c), toilets, boatyard facilities
Dues:	not known
Charge:	yes
Directions:	follow M62 east from M18 to Goole then signs to Sobriety Centre which is adjacent to site

Waters accessed: River Ouse, Humber Estuary and North Sea

Kingston-upon-Hull - Hessle Beach
Tel: (0482) 593385 or (0964) 622473 (after hours) (Harbour Master)

Type:	stone and shingle foreshore
Suits:	light craft which can be manhandled
Availability:	approx. 3 hours either side HW
Restrictions:	none
Facilities:	parking for car and trailer, local rescue group operates nearby
Dues:	none
Charge:	none
Directions:	leave M180 at junction 5 taking A15 over Humber Bridge: site is just downstream of bridge

Waters accessed: River Humber and North Sea

Kingston-upon-Hull - Horsewash Slope, Victoria Pier
Tel: (0482) 593385 or (0964) 622473 (after hours) (Harbour Master)

Type:	stone slope
Suits:	light craft which can be manhandled
Availability:	approx. 2 hours either side HW by prior arrangement with harbour master
Restrictions	narrow access road on a bend and height restriction of approx. 12': site maybe obstructed by shipping lying alongside
Facilities:	no fuel, parking for car but not trailer nearby
Dues:	none
Charge:	none
Directions:	leave M62 at Jct 8 following A63: turn right at crossroads before Myton Bridge and proceed to pier (approx 200 yds); site is just east of Hull Marina
Waters accessed:	River Humber and North Sea

Bridlington - South Shore Slipway, Belvedere Parade
Tel: (0262) 673761

Type:	concrete slipway onto hard sand
Suits:	all craft up to 20' LOA
Availability:	all states of tide from 0800 to 1 hour before sunset 1st Apr-31st Oct
Restrictions:	8 knot speed limit within 300m of LWS mark: water-skiing permitted outside limit; all boats are inspected prior to launch and local regulations concerning insurance and safety equipment must be complied with; access to site is via a locked barrier
Facilities:	fuel from garage, parking for car and trailer, toilets, tractor assistance available, chandlers in town, secure boat park
Dues:	none
Charge:	approx. £3.50 or £5 with tractor assistance
Directions:	follow A166 from York or A165 from Hull
Waters accessed:	North Sea

Bridlington - South Landing, Flamborough

Type:	tarmac slipway onto stone and sand
Suits:	all craft up to 20' LOA
Availability:	all states of tide from 0800 to 1 hour before sunset 1st Apr-31st Oct
Restrictions:	8 knot speed limit within 300m of LWS mark: water-skiing permitted outside limit; all boats are inspected prior to launch and local regulations concerning insurance and safety equipment must be complied with; slip is used by Flamborough RNLI Lifeboat and must be kept clear at all times
Facilities:	fuel from village, parking for car and trailer nearby, toilets (200 yds), chandlers in town
Dues:	none

Charge:	approx. £3.50
Directions:	follow A166 from York or A165 from Hull north through Bridlington; turn onto B1255 east to Flamborough: site is to south of village
Waters accessed:	North Sea

Filey - Filey Coble Landing

Type:	slipway of concrete and stone setts onto sand; at certain times there may be small drop at end of slipway
Suits:	sailing craft and small powered craft
Availability:	all states of tide (approx. 2 hours either side HW for larger craft)
Restrictions:	speed limit within 200m of shore: water-skiing permitted outside this area; boats with engine capacity over 20 hp prohibited
Facilities:	no fuel, parking for car and trailer with permission from Harbour Master/Beach Attendant (c), toilets nearby
Dues:	none
Charge:	yes, payable to Harbour Master/Beach Attendant
Directions:	follow A64 and A1039 from York: site is at north end of sea front
Waters accessed:	North Sea

Scarborough - Harbour Slipway
Tel: (0723) 360684

Type:	concrete slipway with stone setts
Suits:	all craft
Availability:	approx. 3 hours either side HW on payment of fee to Lighthouse Duty Officer
Restrictions:	speed limit: speedboats and water-skiing prohibited: slipway has locked barrier
Facilities:	fuel nearby, parking for car and trailer nearby (c) (trailers must be removed from slipway); toilets, chandlery, outboard repairs and diving supplies nearby
Dues:	approx £6. per day
Charge:	no additional fee
Directions:	follow A64 from York and harbour side road
Waters accessed:	North Sea

Whitby - Whitby Marina, off Langbourne Road
Tel: (0947) 600165

Type:	concrete slipway
Suits:	all craft
Availability:	approx. 4 hours either side of HW
Restrictions:	speed limit: water-skiing prohibited in harbour
Facilities:	diesel nearby, no petrol, parking for car and trailer on site (c), toilets, chandlery on site, diving supplies and outboard repairs nearby
Dues:	approx £7.10
Charge:	no additional fee

Directions: follow A171 east from Middlesbrough or A64/A169 from York: turn right in centre of town past Co-op supermarket
Waters accessed: River Esk and North Sea

Saltburn-by-the-Sea - Seafront

Type: launching over shingle and firm sand
Suits: dinghies only
Availability: approx. 2/3 hours either side HW
Restrictions: exposed sea conditions in onshore winds
Facilities: fuel in village, parking for car and trailer on site (c), toilets
Dues: none
Charge: none
Directions: follow A174 from Whitby or Middlesbrough: site is near pier
Waters accessed: North Sea

Redcar - Seafront

Type: three wide concrete slipways onto firm sand
Suits: small craft
Availability: all states of tide but best 2-3 hours either side HW
Restrictions: exposed conditions in onshore winds, local knowledge is essential
Facilities: fuel in town, parking for car and trailer (c), toilets
Dues: none
Charge: none
Directions: follow A1085 from Middlesbrough
Waters accessed: North Sea

Redcar - South Gare Marine Club, South Gare
Tel: (0642) 491039 or 494099 (evenings) (Secretary R Finch)

Type: concrete slipway with winch and snatch block available
Suits: all craft
Availability: all times except 1 hour either side LWS, by prior arrangement
Restrictions: water-skiing in designated areas: tides may be strong at river mouth; all craft must register with the Harbour Office, Tees Dock Tel: (0642) 452541; access to site is via private road which may be shut at odd times and by locked barrier at entrance to club
Facilities: no fuel, parking for car and trailer (c), toilets
Dues: yes
Charge: approx. £6.00
Directions: follow A1085 from Middlesbrough to Coatham taking 'Sea Front' road at traffic lights by Cowies garage and turning left at round-about: club will be seen on left after about 3 miles; access is via single track private road with passing places
Waters accessed: River Tees and North Sea

Stockton-on-Tees - Corporation Quay

Type: concrete slipway
Suits: all craft up to 20' LOA approx.
Availability: from 3 hours before HW to 1 hour after at present; a barrage is being constructed and when in place site will be useable at all times
Restrictions: water-skiing permitted upstream: all craft must register with the Harbour Office, Tees Dock Tel: (0642) 452541 if using the tidal river downstream of barrage; for further information and permission contact Estates Valuation Office, Stockton-on-Tees BC (0642) 670067: area being developed as a linear water park
Facilities: petrol, parking for car and trailer, further facilities to be provided
Dues: yes below barrage
Charge: none at present
Directions: follow A1(M) north turning off onto A66 and following signs to Stockton: access is via car park in Riverside Road
Waters accessed: River Tees and North Sea

Seaton Carew - Seafront

Type: concrete slipway with slope onto soft sand
Suits: small craft: vehicle assistance required
Availability: approx. 2-3 hours either side HW
Restrictions: all craft must keep clear of shipping channels; exposed conditions in onshore winds; local knowledge is necessary
Facilities: no fuel, parking for car and trailer (c), no toilets
Dues: none
Charge: none
Directions: follow A19 from Teesside, then A689 and B1276 to seafront
Waters accessed: North Sea

Hartlepool - West Harbour Slipway
Tel: (0429) 865744 (Marina Office) for further information

Type: concrete slipway onto shingle and hard sand
Suits: all craft
Availability: approx. 3 hours either side HW
Restrictions: 4 knot speed limit: no mooring or anchoring in West harbour
Facilities: diesel from marina, parking for car and trailer on site, toilets and showers, chandlery, outboard repairs, diving supplies nearby: overnight berths in marina: lock access 4¼ hours either side HW
Dues: none
Charge: none
Directions: follow A19 from Teesside, then A172 , turn right at roundabout, straight across 4 sets of traffic lights then right at 'T' junction: site is on left behind cabins alongside inner North Pier
Waters accessed: Hartlepool Bay and North Sea

Hartlepool - Tees Sailing Club, West Harbour
Tel: (0429) 272192 (1994) (0429) 262249 (1995)

Type:	concrete slipway
Suits:	all craft up to 5 tons
Availability:	approx. 4 hours either side HW, Wed pm, all day Sat and Sun or by prior arrangement
Restrictions:	4 knot speed limit in harbour; no mooring or anchoring permitted in W harbour
Facilities:	diesel from marina, parking for car and trailer and toilets on site; chandlery, outboard repairs, diving supplies, overnight berths and showers in marina; access through lock 4½ hours either side HW
Dues:	none
Charge:	approx. £5.00
Directions:	follow A19 then A689 to town centre, turning right near "The Mail" office down Church St: left at traffic lights over level crossing and proceed until SC on right
Waters accessed:	Hartlepool Bay and North Sea

Hartlepool - Crimdon Caravan Park

Type:	launch from concrete over steeply sloping soft sand onto firm sand
Suits:	very small craft
Availability:	all states of tide
Restrictions:	landrover or similar required to launch, site office must be advised of intention to launch
Facilities:	no fuel, parking for car and trailer (c), toilets
Dues:	none
Charge:	none
Directions:	follow A1086 from Hartlepool north for 3 miles
Waters accessed:	North Sea

Seaham Harbour - Harbour Slipway, North Dock
Tel: (091) 5813877 (Seaham Harbour Dock Co)

Type:	steep concrete slipway
Suits:	all craft up to 24' LOA and 5' draught
Availability:	approx. 2 hours either side HW
Restrictions:	5 knot speed limit: water-skiing prohibited; security must be advised of intention to launch on arrival at site
Facilities:	fuel nearby, parking for car and trailer nearby
Dues:	none
Charge:	approx. £6.00
Directions:	follow A19 north from Middlesbrough, turn onto B1285 site is adjacent to centre of Seaham
Waters accessed:	North Sea

Sunderland - Claxhaugh Rock
Tel: (091) 5140411 (Harbour Master)

Type:	concrete slipway
Suits:	all craft up to 20' LOA
Availability:	approx. 3 hours either side HW
Restrictions:	6 knot speed limit: water-skiing prohibited
Facilities:	no fuel, parking for car and trailer on site
Dues:	approx. £5.52
Charge:	no additional fee
Directions:	from A19 turn onto A183 at sign "Sunderland South": turn left at first roundabout, left at next roundabout: ask for directions when river is reached: site is 4 miles from river mouth
Waters accessed:	River Wear and North Sea

Washington - Fatfield
Tel: (091) 5140411 (Harbour Master)

Type:	concrete slipway
Suits:	all craft up to 20' LOA
Availability:	approx. 3 hours either side HW
Restrictions:	speed limit: water-skiing prohibited; narrow access road
Facilities:	no fuel, parking for car and trailer nearby
Dues:	approx £5.52
Charge:	no additional fee
Directions:	turn off A1(M) south of Washington services onto A195 east turn right onto A182 and follow signs to Fatfield: site is down narrow road on north bank of river opposite Fatfield Club, 9 miles from river mouth
Waters accessed:	River Wear and North Sea

Roker - Inshore Lifeboat Slip, Marine Walk

Type:	short concrete slipway onto soft sandy beach
Suits:	small craft which can be manhandled
Availability:	all states of tide
Restrictions:	6 mph speed limit: no motorised vehicles on beaches:;Inshore Lifeboat launches from ramp which must be kept clear at all times and Inshore Superintendent's Office is on Marine Walk
Facilities:	fuel, parking for car and trailer and toilets nearby; watersports centre for canoes, board sailing etc: nearby
Dues:	approx £4.70 (£26 pa)
Charge:	none
Directions:	follow A183 north from town centre: where Harbour View joins Roker Terrace take Pier View Rd to Marine Walk: site is near North Pier
Waters accessed:	North Sea

Roker - North Dock Marina
Tel: (091) 5144721 (Marina Manager)

Type:	concrete slipway
Suits:	all craft
Availability:	all states of tide
Restrictions:	6 knot speed limit in harbour and river: water-skiing in designated area
Facilities:	fuel from garage, parking for car and trailer, toilets, showers and changing rooms nearby (200 yds); moorings
Dues:	none
Charge:	approx £5.00 (£40.00 pa)
Directions:	from A1 take A690 and A19 north; turn right onto A1231 east to Roker following signs to seafront and Marine Activity Centre: site is at mouth of river
Waters accessed:	North Sea

South Shields - Groyne Launching Ramp, Little Haven Beach
Tel: Easter to Sept (091) 4557411/4546612

Type:	concrete slipway
Suits:	all craft
Availability:	all states of tide except 1 hour either side LWS with permit
Restrictions:	6 knot speed limit: no water-skiing or pwcs in harbour: permit available from Tourist Information Office, Sea Road or from Central Library, Prince George Sq; certificate of 3rd party insurance for £1,000,000 is needed to obtain permit
Facilities:	fuel nearby, parking for car nearby and for trailer on site (c), toilets and diving supplies nearby
Dues:	for 1 day - no charge; for limited period - approx. £6.45
Charge:	approx £6.00 (£25 pa)
Directions:	follow A6115 south from Newcastle,or A1 then A194 to South Shields and follow signs to seafront
Waters accessed:	River Tyne and North Sea

Newcastle-upon-Tyne - Walker Riverside Park, Pottery Bank
Tel: (091) 2655116 (Walker Riverside Activity Centre)

Type:	steep concrete slipway with locked barrier
Suits:	all craft up to 17' LOA
Availability:	approx. 2 hours either side HW: 4 hours notice of intention to launch must be given to Walker Riverside Activity Centre
Restrictions:	6 knot speed limit, steep and narrow access
Facilities:	fuel nearby, parking for car and trailer on site, toilets nearby
Dues:	for 1 day - no charge; for limited period - approx. £6.45
Charge:	none
Directions:	from Newcastle take A186 Walker Road, turn right opposite 'Quicksave' supermarket into Pottery Bank; Walker Riverside

Activity Centre is at end of street and access is through Pottery Bank car park

Waters accessed: River Tyne and North Sea

Gateshead - Friar's Goose Water Sports Club, Green Lane, Felling
Tel: (091) 4692545 or 4692952 (eves)

Type:	concrete slipway
Suits:	all craft
Availability:	approx. 2-3 hours either side HW
Restrictions:	6 knot speed limit
Facilities:	fuel nearby, parking for car and trailer, toilets nearby, moorings
Dues:	for 1 day - no charge; for limited period - approx. £6.45
Charge:	yes
Directions:	follow A6127 from A1(M) into Gateshead: site is on south bank
Waters accessed:	River Tyne and North Sea

Derwenthaugh - Derwenthaugh Marina
Tel: (091) 4140065 (Powerhouse Marine)

Type:	two concrete slipways
Suits:	craft up to 35' LOA approx
Availability:	approx. 4-5 hours either side HW
Restrictions:	6 mph speed limit upstream; fast water zone downsteam; all craft launching must have 3rd party insurance
Facilities:	parking for car and trailer, toilets, chandlers, moorings
Dues:	for 1 day - no charge; for limited period - approx. £6.45
Charge:	approx. £5.00 per day (£55 pa)
Directions:	follow signs from A69: site is on south bank of river at the confluence of the Rivers Tyne and Derwent near Blaydon
Waters accessed:	River Tyne and North Sea

Newburn - Tyne Riverside Country Park, Grange Road
Tel: (091) 2640014 (Newburn Leisure Centre)

Type:	fairly steep concrete slipway
Suits:	small craft
Availability:	approx. 2½ hours either side HW for club members only
Restrictions:	6 mph speed limit: zoned areas for sailing, water-skiing etc but pwc prohibited; number of water-ski craft is restricted
Facilities:	fuel (½ mile), parking for car and trailer, toilets, changing facilities, refreshments and many other facilities available on site
Dues:	for 1 day - no charge; for limited period - approx. £6.45
Charge:	none
Directions:	from A69 take the A6085 for Throckley / Newburn: turn off in Newburn into Grange Road and follow signs
Waters accessed:	River Tyne and North Sea

North Shields - Ferry Slipway
Tel: (091) 2592499 (Mr Hardacre)

Type:	concrete slipway
Suits:	all craft
Availability:	approx. 3-4 hours either side HW (all states for small craft) by prior arrangement
Restrictions:	6 mph speed limit
Facilities:	fuel nearby, parking for car and trailer, toilets, water, chandlery, boat park and moorings on site
Dues:	for 1 day - no charge; for limited period - approx. £6.45
Charge:	approx. £1.00
Directions:	follow A1058 from Newcastle-upon-Tyne: site is adjacent to North Shields ferry landing
Waters accessed:	River Tyne and North Sea

Cullercoats - Harbour Slip
Tel: (091) 2575544 (N Tyneside Council)

Type:	concrete slipway into harbour
Suits:	dinghies and small powercraft
Availability:	approx. 2-3 hours either side HW
Restrictions:	5 knot speed limit inshore: water-skiing prohibited in harbour, site is staffed Whitsun to end Sept and may be congested at peak times
Facilities:	fuel from garage, parking for car in public car park nearby (c) and for trailer on site, toilets,
Dues:	none
Charge:	approx. craft under 10hp - £5.00 (£24 pa), craft over 10hp - £6.00 (£36.00 pa)
Directions:	follow A1058 east from Newcastle-upon-Tyne to Cullercoats
Waters accessed:	North Sea

Seaton Sluice Harbour
Tel: (0670) 542000 (Blyth Valley Council)

Type:	two concrete slipways
Suits:	all craft up to approx. 20' LOA
Availability:	approx. 2 hours either side HW:
Restrictions:	5 mph speed limit in harbour and fairway: water-skiing permitted outside harbour; harbour has narrow entrance and permission to launch must be obtained from Foreshore and Harbour Office
Facilities:	fuel from garage, parking for car and trailer on site, toilets nearby, boat storage area, moorings
Dues:	none
Charge:	approx. £5.70 (£25.60 pa)
Directions:	turn off A1 onto A19 turning off onto A190
Waters accessed:	North Sea

Newbiggin-by-the-Sea - Church Point Access Point Promenade
Tel: (0670) 853811

Type:	concrete slipway onto hard sand
Suits:	all craft
Availability:	all states of tide
Restrictions:	occasional build-up of wind-blown sand normally removed within 48 hours: trailers and vehicles must not be left on beach
Facilities:	fuel from local garage, parking for car and trailer on site, toilets nearby, Beach Information Centre and Rangers on site in summer
Dues:	none
Charge:	none
Directions:	follow A197 to coast from A1 at Morpeth: access is through Church Point car park or adjacent road
Waters accessed:	North Sea

Amble - The Braid
Tel: (0665) 710306 (Harbour Master)

Type:	concrete slipway
Suits:	small to medium sized craft
Availability:	approx. 2-3 hours either side HW
Restrictions:	4 mph speed limit in harbour; water-skiing by arrangement with Harbour Master
Facilities:	fuel, parking for car and trailer, toilets: chandlery and yard facilities available at boatyard nearby
Dues:	approx. £4.89 dailly or £36.66 for annual permit
Charge:	none
Directions:	follow A1068 north towards Alnwick, turning off between Amble and Warkworth: site is adjacent to Marina
Waters accessed:	North Sea

Beadnell

Type:	small wooden ramp onto firm sandy beach
Suits:	craft which can be manhandled: tractor assistance available for larger craft (c)
Availability:	approx. 2-3 hours either side HW
Restrictions:	8 knot speed limit: water-skiing allowed offshore; launching is controlled by car park attendant 0830-1800
Facilities:	fuel from local garage, parking for car and trailer (c), toilets and showers in car park
Dues:	none
Charge:	approx. £3.75 per day, £30.00 pa (pwc £1.50 per day)
Directions:	follow B1340 north from Alnwick: site is adjacent to car park
Waters accessed:	North Sea

Seahouses (North Sunderland) - Harbour Slipway
Tel: (0665) 720033 (Harbour Master)

Type:	concrete slipway onto sand
Suits:	small craft up to 25' LOA
Availability:	all states of tide except 1 hour either side LWS 0845-1830
Restrictions:	3 knot speed limit in harbour: pwc not encouraged; craft must keep clear of ferries to Farne Islands; locked barrier to site and narrow access road down hill to harbour; slip is used to lauch RNLI Lifeboat and must be kept clear at all times; site can be dangerous in adverse weather conditions when barrier is closed and danger flags flying
Facilities:	fuel from local garage, parking for car in parking area (c) and for trailer on beach, toilets nearby, moorings in outer harbour and boat park with nightwatchman at weekends in summer
Dues:	none
Charge:	approx. for boat and up to 2 persons £6.00, additional persons charged at £1 per head
Directions:	follow B1340 north from Alnwick
Waters accessed:	North Sea

Berwick-upon-Tweed - West End Road, Tweedmouth
Tel: (0289) 307404 (Harbour Master).

Type:	concrete slipway onto shingle
Suits:	small craft
Availability:	approx. 2½ hours either side HW
Restrictions:	6 knot speed limit; water-skiing and pwc prohibited
Facilities:	fuel from local garage, parking for car and trailer on roadside only, toilets
Dues:	none
Charge:	none
Directions:	turn off A1: site is adjacent old bridge on south side of River Tweed
Waters accessed:	North Sea

Mainland Scotland

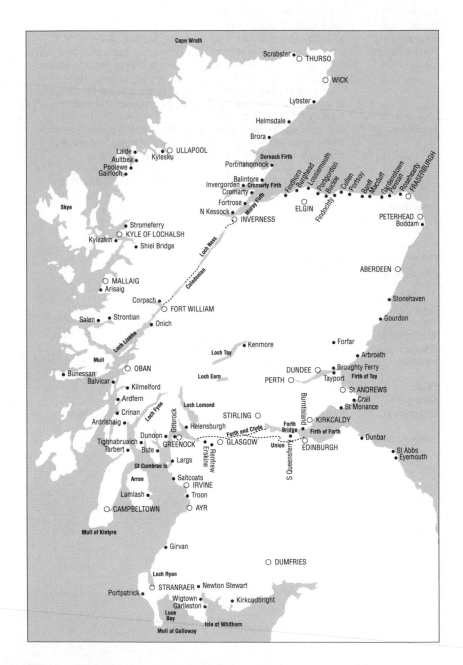

Eyemouth - Harbour Slipway
Tel: (08907) 50223/50248

Type:	steep concrete slipway
Suits:	all craft up to approx. 20' LOA
Availability:	approx. 4 hours either side HW
Restrictions:	5 mph speed limit in harbour: water-skiing permitted offshore; notify harbour master before use
Facilities:	fuel nearby, parking for car and trailer and chandlery on site, toilets, diving supplies and outboard repairs available nearby
Dues:	approx. £2.35
Charge:	no separate fee
Directions:	follow A1 north from Berwick-upon-Tweed to Ayton, turning onto A1107 for 2 miles to Eyemouth
Waters accessed:	North Sea

St Abbs - Harbour Slipway

Type:	concrete slipway onto hard sand
Suits:	all craft
Availability:	approx. 3-4 hours either side HW
Restrictions:	speed limit in harbour: water-skiing permitted offshore; no launching in onshore winds as site is very exposed
Facilities:	fuel (1½ miles), parking for car and trailer, toilets, chandlers in Eyemouth
Dues:	not known
Charge:	yes
Directions:	follow A1 north from Berwick-upon-Tweed turning onto A1107 to Eyemouth, then B6438 at Coldingham: final approach to harbour is steep and narrow
Waters accessed:	North Sea

Dunbar - Harbour Slipway, Victoria Place

Type:	slipway of stone pitching onto level rock and sand
Suits:	all craft
Availability:	approx. 3-4 hours either side HW
Restrictions:	water-skiing prohibited: site is rocky and exposed
Facilities:	fuel nearby, parking for car and trailer on site, toilets, chandlery, diving supplies and outboard repairs nearby
Dues:	approx. £2.00 per day
Charge:	no additional fee
Directions:	follow A1 north from Berwick-upon-Tweed taking A1087 to Dunbar: turn right at 'T' junction at north end of High St
Waters accessed:	Firth of Forth and North Sea

Fisherrow - Harbour Slipway, New Street, Musselburgh

Type:	slipway of stone pitching onto sand
Suits:	all craft
Availability:	all states of tide across sand
Restrictions:	water-skiing prohibited
Facilities:	fuel nearby, parking for car and trailer on site, toilets nearby
Dues:	approx. £2.00 per day
Charge:	no additional fee charged
Directions:	follow A1 east from Edinburgh to Musselburgh, then Harbour Road at A199/ B6415 junction west of River Esk Bridge
Waters accessed:	Firth of Forth and North Sea

Newhaven - Harbour Slipway
Tel: (031) 554 3661 (Leith Harbour Master - Forth Ports Authority)

Type:	cobbled slipway
Suits:	small craft up to approx. 18' LOA
Availability:	approx. 1 hour either side HW
Restrictions:	a permit must be obtained in advance from Forth Ports Authority; jet skis prohibited
Facilities:	fuel from local garage, very limited parking in adjacent roads, toilets
Dues:	yes
Charge:	approx. £13.50 per ft up to 18' (min charge £40)
Directions:	leave M8 at junction 2 taking A8 to Edinburgh city centre then follow signs to Newhaven
Waters accessed:	Firth of Forth and North Sea

Granton - Harbour Slipway
Tel: (031) 554 4343 (Forth Ports Authority)

Type:	cobbled slipway
Suits:	small craft which can be be manhandled
Availability:	approx. 1 hour either side HW
Restrictions:	a permit must be obtained in advance from Forth Ports Authority, and permission to launch from the Piermaster at the end of the Quay; no trailers over 30'
Facilities:	fuel nearby, parking for car and trailer by arrangement, chandlery nearby
Dues:	yes
Charge:	approx. £13.50 per ft up to 18' LOA (min charge £40)
Directions:	leave M8 at junction 2 taking A8 to Edinburgh city centre then follow signs to Granton: site is on east side of Middle Pier
Waters accessed:	Firth of Forth and North Sea

Cramond - Riverside Walk Slipway
Tel: (031) 336 1356 (Cramond Boat Club)

Type:	concrete slipway
Suits:	craft up to 25' LOA
Availability:	approx. 2 hours either side HW
Restrictions:	none
Facilities:	no fuel, parking for car and trailer nearby (c), toilets
Dues:	none
Charge:	yes
Directions:	leave M8 at junction 2, taking A8/A902 and minor roads to Cramond: site is at mouth of river on east bank adjacent Cramond Boat Club

Waters accessed: Firth of Forth and North Sea

South Queensferry - Port Edgar Marina
Tel: (031) 331 3330

Type:	concrete slipway
Suits:	all craft up to 30' LOA
Availability:	approx. 5 hours either side HW, 0830-2200 by prior arrangement
Restrictions:	3 knot speed limit in harbour: water-skiing permitted in designated area downstream
Facilities:	diesel on site, petrol (1 mile), parking for car and trailer, toilets, chandlery and other marina facilities
Dues:	none
Charge:	approx. £1.70 up to 16' LOA and £4.50 over 16' LOA
Directions:	leave M8 at junction 1 taking A8000 and minor roads: site is just west of Forth Bridge

Waters accessed: Firth of Forth and North Sea

North Queensferry - Town Slip

Type:	concrete slipway
Suits:	all craft up to 25' LOA
Availability:	approx. 3-4 hours either side HW
Restrictions:	water-skiing permitted in designated area downstream
Facilities:	parking for car and trailer and toilets
Dues:	none
Charge:	none
Directions:	follow signs to North Queensferry after crossing Forth Bridge: site is between road and rail bridges

Waters accessed: Firth of Forth and North Sea

Aberdour - Shore Road Slipway

Type:	concrete slipway onto beach
Suits:	all craft up to 20' LOA
Availability:	approx. 2 hours either side HW
Restrictions:	none known
Facilities:	fuel, parking for car and trailer
Dues:	none
Charge:	none
Directions:	follow A921 east from the north side of the Forth Bridge: site is at pier
Waters accessed:	Firth of Forth and North Sea

Burntisland - Burntisland Beach

Type:	concrete slipway onto beach
Suits:	small craft
Availability:	all states of tide
Restrictions:	pwc prohibited
Facilities:	fuel nearby, parking for car and trailer, toilets
Dues:	none
Charge:	none
Directions:	follow A921 east from north side of Forth Bridge
Waters accessed:	Firth of Forth and North Sea

Kinghorn - Kinghorn Loch

Type:	concrete slipway
Suits:	dinghies and trailer-sailers
Availability:	at all times with prior permission from Kirkcaldy DC, Town House, Kircaldy
Restrictions:	powerboats prohibited
Facilities:	parking for car and trailer
Dues:	none
Charge:	none
Directions:	follow A921 east from north side of Forth Bridge: site is between Burntisland and Kinghorn near Kinghorn Tannery
Water accessed:	Kinghorn Loch

Kinghorn - Longboat Inn, Pettycur Road

Type:	concrete slipway and crane
Suits:	small craft
Availability:	all states of tide except 1 hour either side LWS
Restrictions:	none known
Facilities:	diesel on site, petrol nearby, parking for car and trailer (c for visi-

tors), toilets

Dues:	none
Charge:	none known
Directions:	follow A921 east from north side of Forth Bridge
Water accessed:	Firth of Forth and North Sea

St Monance - Harbour Slipway
Tel: (0333) 730428

Type:	concrete slipway
Suits:	all craft
Availability:	approx. 2 hours either side HW
Restrictions:	speed limit in harbour: pwc and water-skiing prohibited
Facilities:	fuel from garage (Pittenweem), parking for car and trailer and toilets nearby
Dues:	approx £5.00
Charge:	approx £5.00
Directions:	follow A917/B9131 south of St Andrews to Anstruther, then right onto A917
Waters accessed:	Firth of Forth and North Sea

Anstruther - Harbour Slipway
Tel: (0333) 310836

Type:	concrete slipway
Suits:	all craft up to 30' LOA
Availability:	approx. 3 hours either side HW
Restrictions:	3 knot speed limit in harbour: pwc prohibited; water-skiing prohibited in harbour
Facilities:	fuel nearby, parking for car and trailer (c), toilets and showers on site; chandlery from Pittenweem
Dues:	approx £5.00
Charge:	approx £5.00
Directions:	follow A917/B9131 south of St Andrews
Waters accessed:	Firth of Forth and North Sea

Anstruther - Cellardyke Harbour Slipway
Tel: (0333) 310836

Type:	concrete slipway
Suits:	small craft
Availability:	approx. 3 hours either side HW
Restrictions:	3 knot speed limit in harbour: pwc prohibited; water-skiing allowed outside harbour; narrow entrance to harbour
Facilities:	fuel from Anstruther, limited parking for car and trailer, toilets nearby
Dues:	approx £5.00

Charge: approx £5.00
Directions: follow A917/B9131 south of St Andrews: site is 1 mile east of Anstruther
Waters accessed: Firth of Forth and North Sea

Crail - Harbour Slipway
Tel: (0333) 50277 (Harbour Master)

Type: concrete slipway
Suits: all craft
Availability: approx. 2 hours either side HW
Restrictions: speed limit in harbour: pwc prohibited; no water-skiing in harbour
Facilities: fuel nearby, parking for car and trailer nearby, toilets
Dues: approx £5.00
Charge: approx £5.00
Directions: follow A917 south from St Andrews
Waters accessed: Firth of Forth and North Sea

St Andrews - Harbour Slipway

Type: concrete slipway
Suits: small craft
Availability: approx. 2 hours either side HW
Restrictions: slow speed in harbour: obtain Harbour Master's permission before launching
Facilities: fuel in town, parking for car and trailer, toilets
Dues: yes
Charge: yes
Directions: leave M90 at junction 8 taking the A91 east: follow signs through town to harbour: site is in corner of outer harbour
Waters accessed: North Sea

Tayport - Harbour Slipway
Tel: (0382) 552249 (Tayport Harbour Trust)

Type: slipway of concrete and cobbles
Suits: all craft
Availability: approx. 4 hours either side HW
Restrictions: 5 mph speed limit: advise Secretary Tayport Harbour Trust in writing or by telephone before launching
Facilities: no diesel, petrol nearby, parking for car and trailer, toilets
Dues: none
Charge: approx. £4.00; £10 (week) or £25 (pa)
Directions: leave M90 at junction 8 taking A91 east, then A914 following signs to Tay Bridge: turn right onto B946 before reaching bridge
Waters accessed: River Tay, Firth of Tay and North Sea

Perth - Tay Street, Railway Bridge
Tel: (0738) 39911

Type:	slipway of granite setts
Suits:	dinghies, canoes, pwc
Availability:	all states of tide
Restrictions:	speed limit: access from one-way street; power boats prohibited
Facilities:	fuel nearby, parking in metered bays (c) not on slipway, toilets and outboard repairs nearby
Dues:	none
Charge:	none
Directions:	follow M90 north to Perth, then signs to city centre: at 'T' junction where High St meets Tay St turn south into Tay St: site is on left just before railway bridge

Waters accessed: River Tay, Firth of Tay and North Sea

Perth - Perth Water Ski Club, Shore Road

Type:	concrete slipway
Suits:	all craft up to 25' LOA
Availability:	approx. 2 hours either side HW
Restrictions:	insurance certificate required
Facilities:	fuel, parking for car and trailer (c), chandlery
Dues:	not known
Charge:	yes
Directions:	leave M90 at junction 10 and follow signs to town centre: site is in Shore Road downstream of railway bridge

Waters accessed: River Tay, Firth of Tay and North Sea

Kenmore - Loch Tay Boating Centre, Pier Road
Tel: (0887) 830291

Type:	concrete slipway
Suits:	all craft
Availability:	0900 - 1900 (non-tidal)
Restrictions:	pwc prohibited on Loch Tay
Facilities:	no fuel, parking for car and trailer, toilets, outboard repairs, changing rooms, tearoom all on site
Dues:	approx. £5.50 per day
Charge:	no additional fee charged
Directions:	follow A9 north from Perth, turning left onto A827 to Aberfeldy and Kenmore and turning off in village: site is 100m from main road

Waters accessed: Loch Tay

Tayside - Clatto Country Park

Tel: (0382) 89076 (Countryside Ranger)

Type:	launching into reservoir
Suits:	dinghies and small craft
Availability:	1100-dusk Apr- Sept with day permit from Countryside Ranger
Restrictions:	powercraft prohibited: contact Countryside Ranger in advance
Facilities:	parking for car and trailer, toilets and showers
Dues:	none
Charge:	approx. £2.50 per day
Directions:	from Dundee take A923, crossing A972: at next roundabout turn right, then left and follow signs from Dalmahoy Drive

Waters accessed: reservoir

Tayside - Monikie Country Park

Tel: (0382) 35202 (Countryside Ranger)

Type:	launching into reservoir
Suits:	dinghies and small craft
Availability:	1100-dusk with day or seasonal permit from Countryside Ranger
Restrictions:	powercraft prohibited: contact Countryside Ranger in advance
Facilities:	parking for car and trailer, toilets, showers, changing rooms and limited boat storage
Dues:	none
Charge:	approx. £2.50 per day
Directions:	from Dundee take A92 east, turning left onto B962 and following signs

Waters accessed: lake/reservoir

Broughty Ferry - Harbour Slipway

Type:	cobblestone and concrete slipway
Suits:	all craft up to 25' LOA and larger craft with assistance
Availability:	approx. 3 hours either side HW
Restrictions:	5 knot speed limit inshore with access lanes to designated water-sport area
Facilities:	fuel from Dundee, parking for car and trailer, toilets, chandlers (1 mile)
Dues:	none
Charge:	none
Directions:	follow A390 east from Dundee town centre for 3 miles: site is just east of Broughty Castle

Waters accessed: Firth of Tay and North Sea

Johnshaven - Harbour Slipway
Tel: (0561) 362262 (Harbour Master)

Type:	concrete slipway into outer basin
Suits:	all shallow-draught craft
Availability:	approx. 3 hours either side HW by arrangement with Harbour Master
Restrictions:	speed limit: water-skiing allowed outside harbour; narrow entrance through rocky foreshore can be difficult in winds between NE and SE
Facilities:	no fuel, parking for car and trailer, toilets, chandlery, outboard repairs, electricity, water all on site
Dues:	approx. £6.00
Charge:	no additional fee
Directions:	follow A92 north from Montrose
Waters accessed:	North Sea

Inverbervie - Gourdon Harbour, Gourdon by Montrose
Tel: (0561) 361779 (Harbour Master)

Type:	two steep concrete slipways onto soft mud
Suits:	all craft up to approx. 18' LOA
Availability:	approx. 3 hours either side of HW
Restrictions:	3 knot speed limit in harbour: pwc and water-skiing prohibited; rocky harbour entrance, consult Harbour Master before sailing
Facilities:	petrol nearby, diesel on Fri am, parking for car and trailer, toilets, small boat repairs, diesel engine repairs all on site
Dues:	included in charge
Charge:	approx. £6.00 per day
Directions:	follow A92 north from Montrose: road to harbour has steep hill and sharp bend
Waters accessed:	North Sea

Stonehaven - Harbour Slipway
Tel: (0569) 62741 (Harbour Master)

Type:	concrete slipway onto hard sand in Inner Basin
Suits:	all craft up to approx. 18' LOA
Availability:	approx. 3 hours either side of HW
Restrictions:	3 knot speed limit in harbour: pwc and water-skiing prohibited; can be congested in Summer
Facilities:	petrol nearby, diesel on Fri from tanker, parking for car and trailer and toilets on site, outboard repairs, chandlery and pub nearby
Dues:	included in charge
Charge:	approx. £6.00 per day
Directions:	follow A92 south from Aberdeen and signs to harbour
Waters accessed:	North Sea

Boddam - Harbour Slipway
Tel: (0779) 475494 (Harbour Master)

Type:	concrete slipway
Suits:	all craft
Availability:	approx. 2 hours either side HW
Restrictions:	3 knot speed limit in harbour
Facilities:	petrol, parking for car, short term parking for trailer (100 yds), toilets
Dues:	none
Charge:	approx. £3.00
Directions:	turn off A952 south of Peterhead
Waters accessed:	North Sea

Peterhead - The Lido

Type:	firm sand
Suits:	dinghies and small power boats
Availability:	all states of tide
Restrictions:	water-skiing permitted offshore: access road is steep and fairly narrow
Facilities:	fuel nearby, parking for car on site and trailer nearby, toilets, outboard repairs and diving supplies nearby: marina opening Apr '94
Dues:	none at present
Charge:	none at present
Directions:	turn off A952 north of Aberdeen: site is adjacent to caravan site
Waters accessed:	Peterhead Bay and North Sea

Fraserburgh - Balaclava Inner Harbour
Tel: (0346) 515858 (Harbour Master)

Type:	steep concrete slipway
Suits:	all craft up to 25'LOA
Availability:	approx. 3 hours either side of HW
Restrictions:	speed limit in harbour: access down narrow road; mainly fishing and commercial port is not ideal for recreational use
Facilities:	fuel nearby, parking for car only nearby, toilets nearby, chandlers
Dues:	approx. £5.00 per day
Charge:	no additional fee
Directions:	follow A92 (42 miles) north from Aberdeen and then signs from town centre
Waters accessed:	North Sea

Rosehearty - Harbour Slipway
Tel (0346) 571292 (Harbour Master)

Type:	steep concrete slipway onto firm sand
Suits:	all craft upto 20' LOA

Availability:	all states of tide except 1 hour either side of LWS
Restrictions:	3 knot speed limit in harbour: pwc prohibited but water-skiing permitted offshore; check with Harbour Master before launching
Facilities:	fuel (4 miles), parking for car and trailer on site, toilets and chandlers nearby, pub, caravan site and golf course
Dues:	approx. £6.00 per day
Charge:	no additional fee
Directions:	follow B9031 (4 miles) west from Fraserburgh
Waters accessed:	Moray Firth and North Sea

Pennan - Harbour Slipway

Type:	gentle concrete slipway onto sand and shingle
Suits:	dinghies and small powerboats
Availability:	approx. 2 hours either side of HW
Restrictions:	access to harbour is via steep road and site is very exposed especially in northerly winds
Facilities:	no fuel, very limited parking for car and trailer, toilets
Dues:	not known
Charge:	none
Directions:	follow B9031 10½ miles west from Fraserburgh
Waters accessed:	Moray Firth and North Sea

Gardenstown - Harbour Slipway
Tel: (0261) 851323 (Secretary to Harbour Trustees)

Type:	steep concrete slipway
Suits:	all craft up to 20' LOA
Availability:	approx. 2 hours either side of HW
Restrictions:	5 mph speed limit: water-skiing allowed offshore; site difficult in northerly winds
Facilities:	fuel in village, parking for car and trailer, toilets
Dues:	none
Charge:	approx. £2.50: larger craft approx. £3.50
Directions:	from Fraserburgh follow A98 and B9032/9031 west
Waters accessed:	Moray Firth and North Sea

Macduff - Harbour Slipway
Tel: (0261) 832236 (Harbour Master)

Type:	concrete slipway
Suits:	all shallow draught craft
Availability:	approx. 3 hours either side of HW
Restrictions:	speed limit: water-skiing allowed outside harbour
Facilities:	fuel nearby, parking for car and trailer, toilets, chandlery, diving supplies and outboard repairs all nearby
Dues:	approx. £6.00 per day

Charge: no additional fee
Directions: follow A950 west from Peterhead then A98
Waters accessed: Moray Firth and North Sea

Banff - Harbour Slipway
Tel: (0261) 815093 (Harbour Master)

Type: concrete slipway onto sand
Suits: all craft up to approx. 30' LOA
Availability: approx. 3-4 hours either side HW: consult Harbour Master
Restrictions: 3 knot speed limit: no water-skiing, windsurfing etc within harbour limits; site is exposed in N to ENE winds
Facilities: petrol nearby, diesel from Macduff, parking for car and trailer nearby, toilets on site, chandlery and outboard repairs nearby
Dues: approx. £4.20
Charge: approx. £6.00: 6 month ticket available
Directions: follow A950 west from Peterhead then A98: turn off at bridge between Macduff and Banff: site is in Outer Basin at root of lighthouse pier
Waters accessed: Moray Firth and North Sea

Portsoy - Harbour Slipway
Tel: (0261) 815093 (Harbour Master)

Type: concrete slipway
Suits: all craft up to 30' LOA
Availability: approx. 3-4 hours either side HW: consult Harbour Master
Restrictions: 3 knot speed limit: no water-skiing,windsurfing etc within harbour limits
Facilities: petrol in town, very limited parking for car and trailer, toilets
Dues: approx. £4.20
Charge: approx. £6.00: 6 month ticket available
Directions: follow A950 west from Peterhead then A98 and signs to harbour: site is at west end of harbour
Waters accessed: Moray Firth and North Sea

Cullen - Harbour Slipway
Tel: (0343) 547868 (Harbour Master)

Type: steep concrete slipway onto sandy beach
Suits: all craft up to 20' LOA and draught of 3-4'
Availability: approx. 2 hours either side HW
Restrictions: 3 mph speed limit in harbour: site is very exposed in N to W winds
Facilities: fuel from garage, limited parking for car and trailer, toilets on site, chandlers in Macduff
Dues: none
Charge: none

Directions: follow A950 west from Peterhead then A98: site is at west end of harbour by West Pier

Waters accessed: Moray Firth and North Sea

Portknockie - Inner Basin Slipway
Tel: (0542) 840833 evenings (Harbour Master)

Type:	short concrete slipway
Suits:	small craft
Availability:	approx. 4 hours either side HW
Restrictions:	3 mph speed limit in harbour: road to harbour is steep
Facilities:	fuel, parking for car and trailer, toilets
Dues:	none
Charge:	none
Directions:	follow A96 east from Elgin, then A98, turning left onto A942: site is in inner basin beside Middle Pier

Waters accessed: Moray Firth and North Sea

Findochty - Harbour Slipway
Tel: (0542) 831466 (Harbour Master)

Type:	long concrete slipway
Suits:	all craft up to approx. 25' LOA
Availability:	approx. 2 hours either side HW
Restrictions:	3 mph speed limit in harbour: entrance can be difficult in N winds
Facilities:	parking for car and trailer, toilets nearby, pub
Dues:	none
Charge:	from £2.00 to a max. of £5.00
Directions:	turn off A96 east of Elgin onto A98, turning left onto A942 and following coastal road: site is in inner basin by West Pier

Waters accessed: Moray Firth and North Sea

Buckie - Harbour Slipway
Tel: (0542) 831700 (Harbour Master)

Type:	concrete slipway into No 4 Basin
Suits:	dinghies
Availability:	approx. 3 hours either side HW
Restrictions:	3 mph speed limit in harbour
Facilities:	fuel, parking for car and trailer, toilets, chandlers, crane and winch (100 kg) for hire, repairs
Dues:	none
Charge:	none
Directions:	follow A96 east of Elgin, taking A98 and turning left after 7 miles onto A942

Waters accessed: Moray Firth and North Sea

Portgordon - Harbour Slipway
Tel: (0343) 820213 (Smith Gore - Chartered Surveyors)

Type:	concrete slipway
Suits:	dinghies and small craft
Availability:	approx. 2-3 hours either side HW with prior permission
Restrictions:	site is part of Crown Estate
Facilities:	fuel from local garage, parking for car and trailer adjacent
Dues:	none
Charge:	none
Directions:	turn off A96 east of Elgin, taking A98 and turning onto A990: site is on east side of harbour
Waters accessed:	Moray Firth and North Sea

Lossiemouth - Harbour Slipway
Tel: (0343) 813066 (Harbour Master)

Type:	concrete slipway
Suits:	dinghies and powerboats
Availability:	all states of tide
Restrictions:	3 mph speed limit in harbour
Facilities:	fuel, parking for car and trailer, toilets, chandlers and boatyard: Lossiemouth SC is nearby
Dues:	yes
Charge:	none
Directions:	follow A941 6 miles north from Elgin
Waters accessed:	Moray Firth and North Sea

Hopeman - Harbour Slipway
Tel:(0343) 830650 (Harbour Master)

Type:	steep concrete slipway
Suits:	dinghies and powerboats
Availability:	approx. 2 hours either side HW with prior permission
Restrictions:	3 mph speed limit in harbour
Facilities:	fuel, parking for car and trailer, toilets, chandlers
Dues:	none
Charge:	yes
Directions:	follow A96 east from Inverness, turning onto B9013 between Forres and Elgin then right onto B9012 for 2 miles: site is in inner harbour near West Pier
Waters accessed:	Moray Firth and North Sea

Burghead - Harbour Slipway
Tel: (0343) 835337 (Harbour Master)

Type:	steep concrete slipway onto sandy beach
Suits:	all craft up to 30' LOA
Availability:	all states of tide
Restrictions:	3 knot speed limit in harbour: narrow access road, no water-skiing; this is a commercial and not a recreational harbour
Facilities:	fuel nearby, parking for car and trailer and toilets on site, chandlers nearby, crane for hire
Dues:	none
Charge:	approx. £6.00
Directions:	follow A96 east from Inverness, turning onto B9013 between Forres and Elgin: site is near North Pier
Waters accessed:	Moray Firth and North Sea

Findhorn - Findhorn Boatyard
Tel: (0309) 690099

Type:	concrete slipway
Suits:	all craft
Availability:	all states of tide
Restrictions:	none
Facilities:	fuel from Kinloss, parking for car and trailer, toilets, chandlers, repairs and diving supplies: 12 ton boat holst, winter storage and cafe all on site: Royal Findhorn YC and 2 water-ski clubs nearby
Dues:	none
Charge:	approx. £4.50
Directions:	follow A96 east from Inverness, turning onto B9011 at Forres then left at Kinloss following road through village
Waters accessed:	Moray Firth and North Sea

Inverness - Seaport Marina, Muirtown Wharf (Caledonian Canal)
Tel: (0463) 233140 (Canal Office)

Type:	steep slipway into 5' water
Suits:	all craft suited to use of locks
Availability:	during working hours 0800-1800 daily
Restrictions:	6 mph speed limit: contact Caledonian Canal Office prior to arrival to discuss requirements
Facilities:	fuel nearby, parking for car and trailer by arrangement, toilets chandlery and outboard repairs nearby
Dues:	obtain BW licence from Office
Charge:	none
Directions:	follow A9 to Inverness, then signs to Muirtown, turning right before bridge
Waters accessed:	Loch Ness and Caledonian Canal

Inverness - Caley Marina, Canal Road
Tel: (0463) 236539

Type:	fairly steep slipway into 6' water
Suits:	craft up to 21' LOA
Availability:	during working hours 0830-1730 mon to sat: at other times by prior arrangement
Restrictions:	6 mph speed limit
Facilities:	diesel, parking for car and trailer (c), toilets, overnight moorings, chandlery, engine repairs and boatyard with crane by arrangement
Dues:	obtain BW licence from Office
Charge:	yes
Directions:	leave A9 following signs for the A862 across Inverness to Muirtown swing bridge: turn up Canal Road by the flight of locks
Waters accessed:	Caledonian Canal and Loch Ness

Inverness - Tomnahurich Bridge

Type:	steep slipway into 5' water
Suits:	all craft
Availability:	0800-1800 daily
Restrictions:	6 mph speed limit
Facilities:	fuel nearby
Dues:	obtain BW licence from Canal Office at Seaport Marina, Muirtown
Charge:	yes
Directions:	turn right off A82 at Tomnahurich Bridge
Waters accessed:	Caledonian Canal and Loch Ness

South Laggan - Great Glen Water Park
Tel: (08093) 223

Type:	steep slipway into approx. 4' water
Suits:	all craft
Availability:	0900-2100 daily
Restrictions:	6 mph speed limit in canal
Facilities:	no fuel, parking for car and trailer (c), water, toilets, overnight moorings, boatyard, restaurant and self catering accomodation
Dues:	none for Loch Oich but obtain BW licence from Canal Office at Seaport Marina, Muirtown for canal
Charge:	yes
Directions:	from Fort William follow A82 for 22 miles north, turning right just before South Laggan swing bridge: site is at south west end of Loch Oich
Waters accessed:	Loch Oich and Caledonian Canal

North Kessock - Old Ferry Pier

Type:	concrete slipway
Suits:	all craft up to 20' LOA
Availability:	approx. 3 hours either side HW
Restrictions:	none known
Facilities:	fuel, parking for car and trailer, toilets, chandlers
Dues:	none
Charge:	none
Directions:	follow A9 north from Inverness: site is on north shore of Beauly Firth upstream of bridge: site is adjacent Inverness Boat Centre
Waters accessed:	Beauly Firth, Moray Firth and North Sea

South Kessock - Old Ferry Pier

Type:	concrete slipway
Suits:	all craft up to 20' LOA
Availability:	approx. 3 hours either side HW
Restrictions:	slip must be kept clear at all times for lifeboat launching
Facilities:	fuel, parking for car and trailer
Dues:	none
Charge:	none
Directions:	turn off A82 in Inverness: site is on south shore of Beauly Firth upstream of bridge:
Waters accessed:	Beauly Firth, Moray Firth and North Sea

Fortrose Harbour - Chanonry Sailing Club Slipway
Tel: (0381) 20861 (Harbour Master) or (0351) 621010 (Sailing Club)

Type:	two concrete slipways on either side of harbour
Suits:	all craft up to 20' LOA
Availability:	approx. 3 hours either side HW
Restrictions:	7 knot speed limit inshore: pwc prohibited
Facilities:	no fuel, limited parking for car and trailer (c), toilets (100 yds); temporary membership of club available with use of clubhouse
Dues:	yes
Charge:	approx. £3.00
Directions:	follow A9 north from Inverness, then A832
Waters accessed:	Moray Firth and North Sea

Cromarty - The Pier
Tel: (0387) 600502 (Harbour Master)

Type:	cobblestone slipway
Suits:	all craft up to 20'LOA
Availability:	at HW only
Restrictions:	none known
Facilities:	fuel, parking for car and trailer, toilets
Dues:	none
Charge:	none
Directions:	follow A9 north from Inverness, then A832
Waters accessed:	Cromarty Firth, Moray Firth and North Sea

Cromarty - The Beach
Tel: (0387) 600502 (Harbour Master)

Type:	launching over shingle and firm sand
Suits:	small craft which can be manhandled or larger craft with 4-wheel drive vehicles
Availability:	all states of tide
Restrictions:	none known
Facilities:	fuel from garage, parking for car and trailer, toilets and shops
Dues:	none
Charge:	none
Directions:	follow A9 north from Inverness, then A832
Waters accessed:	Cromarty Firth, Moray Firth and North Sea

Rosskeen - Slipway
Tel: (0349) 852308 (Cromarty Firth Port Authority)

Type:	concrete slipway
Suits:	all craft
Availability:	approx. 3 hours either side HW
Restrictions:	water-skiing allowed with prior permission of Harbour Master
Facilities:	fuel (3 miles), parking for car and trailer
Dues:	none
Charge:	none
Directions:	follow A9 north from Inverness and along north shore of Cromarty Firth, turning off onto B817: site is just west of Invergordon
Waters accessed:	Cromarty Firth and North Sea

Balintore - Harbour Slipway

Type:	concrete slipway onto hard sand
Suits:	small craft
Availability:	all states of tide

Restrictions:	none known
Facilities:	no fuel, parking for car and trailer, toilets, chandlers
Dues:	none
Charge:	yes
Directions:	follow A9 north from Inverness, turning off south of Tain onto B9165/6
Waters accessed:	Moray Firth and North Sea

Hilton - The Slipway

Type:	concrete slipway
Suits:	small craft
Availability:	approx. 3 hours either side HW
Restrictions:	none known
Facilities:	no fuel, limited parking in street, chandlers in Balintore
Dues:	none
Charge:	yes
Directions:	follow A9 north from Inverness, turning off south of Tain onto B9165/6: site is 1 mile east of Balintore
Waters accessed:	Moray Firth and North Sea

Portmahomack - Harbour Slipway
Tel: (0862) 87441 (Harbour Master)

Type:	stone slipway into small drying harbour
Suits:	all craft up to 20' LOA
Availability:	approx. 3 hours either side HW
Restrictions:	speed limit in harbour: water-skiing allowed offshore; contact Harbour Master/ local shop for permission
Facilities:	petrol, parking for car and trailer, toilets
Dues:	not known
Charge:	yes
Directions:	turn off south of Tain onto B9165
Waters accessed:	Dornoch Firth, Moray Firth and North Sea

Brora - Harbour Slipway

Type:	concrete slipway with heavy duty hand winch
Suits:	all craft
Availability:	approx. 2½ hours either side HW
Restrictions:	none known
Facilities:	fuel from garage, parking for car and trailer (c)
Dues:	not known
Charge:	yes
Directions:	follow A9 north from Inverness, then minor road south of bridge to river mouth
Waters accessed:	Moray Firth and North Sea

Helmsdale - Harbour Slipway
Tel: (0431) 2347

Type:	concrete slipway
Suits:	craft up to approx. 18' LOA
Availability:	approx. 3 hours either side HW by prior arrangement
Restrictions:	speed limit in harbour: water-skiing offshore, contact Harbour Master
Facilities:	fuel, parking for car and trailer and toilets nearby
Dues:	yes
Charge:	yes
Directions:	follow A9 north, turn right north of Helmsdale river bridge into Dunrobin St: next right down to Shore St, then left: site is at east end of harbour
Waters accessed:	Moray Firth and North Sea

Lybster - Harbour Slipway

Type:	wooden ramp
Suits:	all craft
Availability:	approx. 2 hours either side HW
Restrictions:	slow speed in harbour: site exposed in onshore winds
Facilities:	fuel nearby, parking for car and trailer
Dues:	none
Charge:	none
Directions:	follow A9 south from Wick, turning off to village and harbour
Waters accessed:	Moray Firth and North Sea

Scrabster - Thurso Bay
Tel: (0847) 62779 (Harbour Master)

Type:	concrete slipway
Suits:	all craft up to 25' LOA
Availability:	approx. 3 hours either side HW
Restrictions:	none
Facilities:	diesel on site, petrol (1½ miles), parking for car and trailer (c), toilets, chandlery, diving supplies and outboard repairs all available nearby
Dues:	approx. £8.81 for 3 days
Charge:	no additional fee
Directions:	follow A882 north west from Wick: site is on west side Thurso Bay
Waters accessed:	Pentland Firth

Kylesku South - Ferry Slipway

Type:	concrete slipway
Suits:	all craft
Availability:	approx. 5 hours either side HW
Restrictions:	none
Facilities:	no fuel, parking for car and trailer nearby, toilets nearby,
Dues:	yes
Charge:	yes
Directions:	from Ullapool follow A835, A837 and A894 north: site is at south side of old ferry crossing
Waters accessed:	Locha' Chairn Bhain, Loch Glendhu, and Loch Glencoul

Laide

Type:	stone and concrete slipway
Suits:	small craft
Availability:	approx. 3 hours either side HW
Restrictions:	not known
Facilities:	fuel from garage, limited parking for car but not trailer, toilets
Dues:	none
Charge:	yes
Directions:	from Inverness follow A9 and A835 north then A832 west to west shore of Gruinard Bay: site is ½ mile from Post Office
Waters accessed:	Gruinard Bay

Aultbea

Type:	stone and concrete slipway
Suits:	small craft
Availability:	approx. 3 hours either side HW
Restrictions:	not known
Facilities:	fuel, limited parking for car, leave trailer by arrangement, toilets
Dues:	none
Charge:	none
Directions:	from Inverness follow A9 and A835 north then A832 west to east side of Loch Ewe: site is near Aultbea Hotel
Waters accessed:	Loch Ewe

Poolewe

Type:	stone and concrete slipway
Suits:	small craft
Availability:	all states of tide except LWS
Restrictions:	none known
Facilities:	no fuel, limited parking for car and trailer by arrangement

Dues:	none
Charge:	none
Directions:	from Inverness follow A9 and A835 north then A832 west to south side of Loch Ewe
Waters accessed:	Loch Ewe

Strath, Gairloch

Type:	stone and concrete slipway
Suits:	small craft up to 18' LOA
Availability:	all states of tide except LWS
Restrictions:	none known
Facilities:	no fuel or parking for car and trailer
Dues:	none
Charge:	yes
Directions:	from Inverness follow A9 and A835 north then A832 west to Gairloch: turn onto B8021: site is on north shore of Loch Gairloch
Waters accessed:	Loch Gairloch

Gairloch - Pier Road
Tel: (0445) 2140 (Pier Master)

Type:	launching from tarmac surface over rock
Suits:	all craft up to 30' LOA
Availability:	approx. 3 hours either side HW or HW only for larger craft
Restrictions:	no speed limit: water-skiing permitted; contact Pier Master for further information
Facilities:	fuel at pier by arrangement, parking for car and trailer, toilets, chandlery, repairs and engineering: temporary membership of club adjacent to slipway allows use of facilities
Dues:	none
Charge:	yes
Directions:	from Inverness follow A9 and A835 north then A832 west to Gairloch: site is on east side of Loch
Waters accessed:	Loch Gairloch

Badachro

Type:	stone and concrete slipway
Suits:	all craft up to 20' LOA
Availability:	approx. 3 hours either side HW
Restrictions:	none known
Facilities:	no fuel, very limited parking for car only
Dues:	none
Charge:	yes
Directions:	from Inverness follow A9 and A835 north then A832 west and turn onto B8056 to south shore of Loch Gairloch
Waters accessed:	Loch Gairloch

Stromeferry - Old Ferry Stage

Type:	concrete slipway
Suits:	all craft
Availability:	approx. 3 hours either side HW
Restrictions:	none known
Facilities:	no fuel, parking for car and trailer
Dues:	not known
Charge:	yes
Directions:	from Fort William take A82 north to Invergarry then A87 west and A890 north: site is at old ferry site on south shore of Loch Carron

Waters accessed: Loch Carron

Kyle of Lochalsh - Old Ferry Slipway
Tel: (0599) 4167 (Harbour Master)

Type:	stone and concrete slipway
Suits:	all craft
Availability:	all states of tide except LWS
Restrictions:	contact Harbour Master (ferry office) for permission to launch
Facilities:	fuel nearby, parking for car and trailer, toilets, outboard repairs and chandlery
Dues:	not known
Charge:	none at present
Directions:	from Fort William take A82 north to Invergarry then A87 west

Waters accessed: Loch Alsh and Inner Sound

Shiel Bridge

Type:	stone slipway
Suits:	all craft
Availability:	approx. 2 hours either side HW
Restrictions:	none known
Facilities:	fuel, parking for car and trailer
Dues:	none
Charge:	none
Directions:	from Fort William take A82 north to Invergarry then A87 west: site is at head of loch opposite Kintail Lodge Hotel

Waters accessed: Loch Duich

Isle of Skye, Kyleakin - Old Ferry Slipway
Tel: (0599) 4167 (Harbour Master)

Type:	concrete slipway
Suits:	all craft
Availability:	all states of tide except LWS
Restrictions:	contact Harbour Master at Kyle of Lochalsh
Facilities:	fuel nearby, parking for car and trailer, chandlery and other facilities at Kyle of Lochalsh
Dues:	none
Charge:	none at present
Directions:	follow A850 south from Portree: site is adjacent ferry slip
Waters accessed:	Loch Alsh and Inner Sound

Isle of Skye - Ardvasar Bay (Sleat Marine Services)
Tel: (04714) 216/387

Type:	slipway onto hard beach of sand and shingle
Suits:	all craft up to 30' LOA
Availability:	all states of tide: check for availability
Restrictions:	speed limit: slip may be obstructed
Facilities:	fuel and parking for car and trailer nearby (c), toilets, limited chandlery and outboard repairs all on site
Dues:	none
Charge:	none
Directions:	from Portree follow A850 south to Broadford then A851 or by ferry from Mallaig: site is opposite village stores
Waters accessed:	Sound of Sleat

Isle of Skye - Stein, Waternish

Type:	narrow concrete slipway
Suits:	small craft
Availability:	approx. 4 hours either side HW
Restrictions:	no water-skiing on Sun: access is via narrow roads
Facilities:	fuel from garage, limited parking for car and trailer
Dues:	none
Charge:	yes
Directions:	from Portree follow A850 north west then B886: site is on western side of Waternish Peninsula
Waters accessed:	Loch Bay

Mallaig - Harbour Slipway
Tel: (0687) 2150

Type:	narrow and fairly steep concrete slipway
Suits:	sailing dinghies, trailer-sailers and canoes
Availability:	approx. 3 hours either side HW
Restrictions:	speed limit: no water-skiing; narrow access
Facilities:	fuel nearby, parking for car and trailer on site, toilets, chandlers and outboard repairs nearby
Dues:	none
Charge:	none
Directions:	follow A830 west from Fort William: site is located south east from harbour adjacent to car park
Waters accessed:	Sound of Sleat

Arisaig Harbour - Arisaig Maritime Ltd
Tel: (06875) 224

Type:	concrete slipway with rails
Suits:	all craft up to 20' LOA
Availability:	approx. 4 hours either side HW 0900-1800
Restrictions:	water-skiing allowed with permission
Facilities:	diesel on site, parking for car and trailer, crane and winch for hire, toilets, limited chandlery, repairs, moorings, shop, hotel, restaurant and accomodation
Dues:	included in launching fee
Charge:	approx. £4.70
Directions:	follow A830 west from Fort William; road has 12½' height restriction
Waters accessed:	Loch nan Ceall

Salen - Loch Sunart Marine Services
Tel: (096 785) 648

Type:	launching from granite jetty (1) or shingle foreshore into creek (2)
Suits:	all craft
Availability:	(1) approx. 3 hours either side HW (2) all states of tide
Restrictions:	none known
Facilities:	fuel (2 miles), parking for car and trailer (c), chandlery
Dues:	none
Charge:	yes
Directions:	from Fort William follow either A830 west taking A861 at Lochailort and B8007 in Salen or take A82 south crossing Loch Linnhe on Corran Ferry and follow A861 via Strontian to Salen: site is on north shore of Loch Sunart on the Ardnamurchan Peninsula
Waters accessed:	Loch Sunart

Resipole - Resipole Farm Caravan Park
Tel: (096 785) 235 (Reception)

Type:	concrete slipway
Suits:	all craft up to 20' LOA
Availability:	approx. 3 hours either side HW by prior arrangement
Restrictions:	overhead telephone cable beside main road
Facilities:	fuel (4 miles), parking for car and trailer and toilets on site, chandlery (2 miles), self-contained accomodation, caravan park, restaurant and bar on site
Dues:	none
Charge:	approx. £5.00
Directions:	from Fort William follow either A830 west taking A861 at Lochailort or A82 south crossing Loch Linnhe on Corran Ferry and take A861 via Strontian: site is 8 miles west of Strontian

Waters accessed: Loch Sunart

Fort William - Corpach
Tel: (0397) 772861 (Corpach Boatbuilding Co Ltd - Sandy Edmonds)

Type:	concrete slipway onto hard beach
Suits:	all craft up to 30' LOA
Availability:	all states of tide except LWS (see restrictions)
Restrictions:	working boatyard: permission to launch must be obtained before use; no water-skiing
Facilities:	no fuel, very limited parking for car and trailer
Dues:	none
Charge:	approx. £10
Directions:	follow A830 west from Fort William along north shore of Loch Eil

Waters accessed: Loch Eil, Loch Linnhe and Caledonian Canal via lock

Fort William - Lochaber Yacht Club, Achintore Road
Tel: (0397) 702370

Type:	concrete slipway with steep access
Suits:	sailing dinghies and small trailer-sailers only
Availability:	all states of tide by prior arrangement
Restrictions:	keep clear of all YC launching and recovery activities
Facilities:	fuel (1 mile), parking for car ($\frac{1}{2}$ mile), parking for trailer on site (c)
Dues:	none
Charge:	approx. £10.00
Directions:	follow A82 south from Fort William town centre ($\frac{1}{2}$ mile): site is at junction with Ashburn Lane

Waters accessed: Loch Linnhe

North Ballachulish - Old Ferry slipway

Type:	concrete slipway
Suits:	all craft up to 20' LOA
Availability:	approx. 5 hours either side HW
Restrictions:	strong current
Facilities:	fuel in village, very limited parking for car and trailer, hotels nearby
Dues:	none
Charge:	none
Directions:	follow A82 south from Fort William, turning left onto B863 before bridge over Loch Leven then right into Old Ferry Rd: site is at end of road close to bridge
Waters accessed:	Loch Leven and Loch Linnhe

South Ballachulish - Laroch

Type:	concrete slipway
Suits:	all craft up to 25' LOA
Availability:	approx. 5 hours either side HW
Restrictions:	strong current
Facilities:	fuel in village, limited parking for car and trailer in lay-by, hotels nearby
Dues:	none
Charge:	none
Directions:	follow A82 south from Fort William, turn onto A828: site is underneath road bridge opposite Ballachulish Hotel
Waters accessed:	Loch Leven and Loch Linnhe

Kentallen - Holly Tree Hotel
Tel: (063174) 292

Type:	concrete slipway
Suits:	all craft
Availability:	approx. 4 hours either side of HW
Restrictions:	use by prior arrangement with hotel proprietor
Facilities:	no fuel, parking for car, leave trailer by arrangement with hotel, accomodation and restaurant
Dues:	none known
Charge:	none known
Directions:	follow A82 and A828 south from Fort William: site is 3 miles south of Ballachulish Bridge on east shore of Loch Linnhe near pier
Waters accessed:	Loch Linnhe

Type:	concrete slipway
Suits:	all craft
Availability:	all states of tide
Restrictions:	none known
Facilities:	fuel, parking for car and trailer, toilets, showers, chandlers
Dues:	none
Charge:	yes
Directions:	site is 1½ miles west of Bunessan off the A849 on north side of Ross of Mull peninsula

Waters accessed: Loch na Lathaich

Barcaldine - Creran Moorings
Tel: (063172) 265

Type:	concrete slipway
Suits:	all craft up to 25' LOA
Availability:	all states of tide except for 1 hour either side LWS
Restrictions:	charge for parking when left for period of time
Facilities:	fuel (6 miles), parking for car and trailer, toilets, showers, moorings, camping, chalets/caravans to let
Dues:	none
Charge:	approx. £10 (DIY), £30 with tractor assistance
Directions:	from Oban follow A828 north: site is 1 mile north of Sea Life Centre

Waters accessed: Loch Creran, Loch Linnhe and Scottish West Coast

Dunstaffnage - Dunstaffnage Yacht Haven
Tel: (0631) 66555

Type:	concrete slipway
Suits:	all craft up to 30' LOA
Availability:	approx. 2 hours either side HW
Restrictions:	none known
Facilities:	no fuel, parking for car and trailer (c), toilets, showers, moorings, restaurant, chandlery and travel hoist
Dues:	none
Charge:	approx. £23.50
Directions:	from Oban take A85 north for 2 miles

Waters accessed: Firth of Lorn and Scottish West Coast

Oban - Ganavan Sands Caravan Park
Tel:(0631) 62179

Type:	wide concrete slipway
Suits:	all craft
Availability:	most states of tide 0830-2000
Restrictions:	speed limit, pwc prohibited, water-skiing permitted offshore
Facilities:	fuel (2 miles), parking for car and trailer (c), toilets, diving supplies, bar, restaurant, touring caravan site and small shop on site: chandlery and outboard repairs in Oban (2 miles)
Dues:	none
Charge:	approx. £6.00
Directions:	from Oban follow the Esplanade coast road north for 2 miles
Waters accessed:	Firth of Lorn and Scottish West Coast

Oban - Railway Pier Slipway
Tel: (0631) 62285 (Caledonian MacBrayne)

Type:	concrete slipway
Suits:	dinghies and powercraft
Availability:	approx. 2 hours either side HW
Restrictions:	speed limit in harbour: water-skiing permitted outside harbour
Facilities:	fuel nearby, limited parking (c), toilets, diving supplies and outboard repairs nearby, chandlers in town (Nancy Black)
Dues:	none
Charge:	none
Directions:	from Glasgow take A82 north then A85 west, following signs in town to car ferries: site is at south of town at end of railway pier
Waters accessed:	Oban Bay and Scottish West Coast

Oban - Port Beag Slip
Tel: (0631) 64142 (Puffin Dive Centre)

Type:	wide steep concrete slipway
Suits:	powercraft only
Availability:	approx. 5 hours either side HW
Restrictions:	slip may be blocked in winter by laid-up boats; water-skiing allowed outside harbour
Facilities:	fuel nearby, parking for car and trailer (½ mile), chandlery in town
Dues:	none
Charge:	none
Directions:	from Glasgow take A82 north then A85 west to Oban and follow Gallanach Rd: site is west of south pier
Waters accessed:	Oban Bay and Scottish West Coast

Oban - Port Nan Cuile - (Oban Marine Centre)
Tel: (0631) 62472

Type:	2 concrete slipways
Suits:	trailer-sailers and powercraft
Availability:	all states of tide
Restrictions:	not suitable for sailing dinghies; mainly a diving centre
Facilities:	fuel, parking for car and trailer (c), toilets, chandlery, diving supplies and overnight moorings all on site
Dues:	none
Charge:	approx. £2.50
Directions:	from Glasgow take A82 north then A85 west to Oban and follow road to Gallanach
Waters accessed:	Sound of Mull and Scottish West Coast

Ford

Type:	concrete slipway
Suits:	all craft
Availability:	at all times
Restrictions:	site is owned by Ford Motor Club and there is locked barrier; obtain key from Ford Motor Hotel: access is via narrow roads
Facilities:	none known
Dues:	none
Charge:	yes
Directions:	from Lochgilphead take A816 north, turning onto B840: site is at southern end of Loch Awe
Waters accessed:	Loch Awe

Lerags - Ardoran Marine
Tel: (0631) 66123

Type:	concrete slipway
Suits:	all craft up to 30' LOA
Availability:	approx. 3 hours either side HW by prior arrangement
Restrictions:	speed limit: no water-skiing; access is via single track road
Facilities:	diesel on site, petrol nearby, parking for car and trailer (phone first), toilets, chandlery, outboard repairs on site, cranage and storage, diving supplies nearby
Dues:	none
Charge:	approx. £8.81 (includes parking)
Directions:	from Oban follow A816 south turning off onto minor road to Lerags
Waters accessed:	Loch Feochan, Firth of Lorn and Scottish West Coast

Balvicar, Isle of Seil - Balvicar Boatyard
Tel: (085 23) 557

Type:	two concrete slipways
Suits:	all craft
Availability:	approx. 5 hours either side of HW by prior arrangement
Restrictions:	yard work has priority; water-skiing allowed away from moorings
Facilities:	fuel nearby, parking for car and trailer on site, toilets, chandlery, diving supplies and engine repairs all available nearby, winter storage, moorings, hoists etc available for boats up to 50' and 30 tons
Dues:	none
Charge:	approx. £5.00
Directions:	from Oban follow A816 south then B844 for 7 miles, turning left at Balvicar village stores

Waters accessed: Seil Sound, Loch Melfort and Scottish West Coast

Kilmelford - Kilmelford Yacht Haven
Tel: (085 22) 248

Type:	concrete slipway or shingle hard
Suits:	all craft up to approx. 45' LOA
Availability:	all states of tide mon - sat 0830 - 1700 or at other times by prior arrangement
Restrictions:	check with boatyard before use
Facilities:	fuel, parking for car and trailer (c), toilets, travel hoist
Dues:	none
Charge:	only if hoist used
Directions:	from Oban take A816 south for 16 miles

Waters accessed: Loch Melfort and Scottish West Coast

Melfort - The Pier (Melfort Pier and Harbour Co)
Tel: (085 22) 333

Type:	three concrete slipways
Suits:	all craft up to 25' LOA
Availability:	all states of tide by prior arrangement
Restrictions:	none known
Facilities:	diesel on site, petrol nearby, parking for car and trailer (c), toilets, showers, launderette, engine repairs, water, electricity, accomodation, restaurant and bar nearby
Dues:	none
Charge:	approx. £12
Directions:	from Oban take A816 south to Kilmelford then minor road to Melfort

Waters accessed: Loch Melfort and Scottish West Coast

Craobh Haven - Craobh Haven Marina
Tel: (085 25) 222

Type:	concrete slipway with hoist for larger craft up to 15 tons
Suits:	all craft up to 45' LOA
Availability:	all states of tide during working hours
Restrictions:	5 mph speed limit in harbour: water-skiing prohibited
Facilities:	diesel on site, parking for car and trailer (c), toilets, showers, launderette, engine repairs, water, electricity, chandlery, restaurant and bar, pontoon berths
Dues:	none
Charge:	approx. £10
Directions:	from Oban take A816 south towards Lochgilphead
Waters accessed:	Loch Shuna and Scottish West Coast

Ardfern - Ardfern Yacht Centre
Tel: (085 25) 247 / 636

Type:	concrete slipway onto shingle
Suits:	all craft up to 35' LOA
Availability:	approx. 3 hours either side HW during working hours (0830-1730)
Restrictions:	use by prior arrangement if possible: water-skiing outside harbour
Facilities:	diesel on site, parking for car and trailer, toilets, showers, water, electricity, bar and restaurant
Dues:	none
Charge:	approx. £12.00 including car parking
Directions:	from Oban follow A816 south, turning onto B8002 for 1 mile: site is on north shore of Loch Craignish
Waters accessed:	Loch Craignish, Sound of Jura and Scottish West Coast

Crinan - Crinan Ferry

Type:	stone slipway
Suits:	all craft up to 30' LOA
Availability:	approx. 2-3 hours either side HW
Restrictions:	none known
Facilities:	fuel, parking for car and trailer, toilets, chandler nearby, larger craft can be launched at Crinan Boatyard: contact Crinan Harbour Association Tel: (054 683) 232 for information
Dues:	none known
Charge:	none
Directions:	from Oban follow A816 south, turning onto B8025 south of Kilmartin then right at 'T' junction onto B841: site is old ferry ramp at end of Crinan Canal near Crinan Hotel
Waters accessed:	Loch Crinan

178

Type:	not known
Suits:	all craft
Availability:	all states of tide
Restrictions:	none known
Facilities:	none known
Dues:	none
Charge:	none
Directions:	from Oban follow A816 south, turn onto B8025 south of Kilmartin then right at 'T' junction onto B841 and left onto B8025: site is on west shore of loch and access is via narrow roads
Waters accessed:	Loch Sween, Sound of Jura and Scottish West Coast

Ardrishaig - Pier Square Slipway (Crinan Canal)
Tel: (0546 60) 3210 (Canal Office)

Type:	steep concrete slipway
Suits:	all craft up to 18' LOA
Availability:	approx. 3 hours either side HW 0900-1700
Restrictions:	speed limit: water-skiing permitted in Loch Fyne; permission to use must be obtained from canal office, information pack available; narrow access
Facilities:	fuel, parking for car and trailer, toilets and other marina facilities nearby
Dues:	contact Canal Office
Charge:	contact Canal Office
Directions:	from Lochgilphead follow A83 south: site is adjacent to main car park and pier at east end of Crinan Canal
Waters accessed:	Crinan Canal, Loch Fyne, and Scottish West Coast

Tarbert - Pier Road
Tel: (0880) 820376 (TYC Secretary: Ian MacGillvray)

Type:	concrete slipway onto shingle
Suits:	all craft up to 25' LOA
Availability:	all states of tide
Restrictions:	4 knot speed limit in harbour: water-skiing permitted outside harbour
Facilities:	fuel and parking for car and trailer nearby (c), toilets; chandlery, diving supplies and outboard repairs in Tarbert
Dues:	none
Charge:	approx. £1.00
Directions:	from Lochgilphead follow A83 south: site is on south side of harbour in Pier Road adjacent Tarbert Yacht Club
Waters accessed:	Loch Fyne and Scottish West Coast

Campbeltown Harbour - New Quay Slip, Hall Street

Tel: (0586) 552552 (Harbour Master)

Type:	concrete slipway
Suits:	all craft up to 30' LOA
Availability:	approx. 2 hours either side HW
Restrictions:	water-skiing at Harbour Master's discretion
Facilities:	fuel, parking for car and trailer, toilets, chandlery and outboard repairs nearby
Dues:	none
Charge:	none
Directions:	from Lochgilphead follow A83 south: site is at head of New Quay and is visible from main roundabout at approach to harbour area
Waters accessed:	Campbeltown Loch and Scottish West Coast

Isle of Arran, Lamlash - Harbour Slipway

Type:	concrete slipway
Suits:	all craft up to 25' LOA
Availability:	approx. 3 hours either side HW
Restrictions:	none known
Facilities:	fuel, parking for car and trailer, toilets, chandlery
Dues:	none
Charge:	none
Directions:	from Glasgow follow A738 or A737 south, then A78 north to Ardrossan, ferry to Brodick then A841 south: site is on harbour front
Waters accessed:	Firth of Clyde and Scottish West Coast

Isle of Arran, Whiting Bay - Shore Road

Type:	concrete slipway
Suits:	dinghies only
Availability:	approx. 2½ hours either side HW
Restrictions:	none known
Facilities:	fuel, parking for car and trailer, toilets, chandlery
Dues:	none
Charge:	none
Directions:	from Glasgow follow A738 or A737 south, then A78 north to Ardrossan, ferry to Brodick then A841 south: site is adjacent to pier
Waters accessed:	Firth of Clyde and Scottish West Coast

Crarae - Quarry Point Visitor Centre

Type: launching over shingle
Suits: all craft up to 20' LOA
Availability: approx. 3 hours either side HW 1000 - 1800 Apr to Oct
Restrictions: none known
Facilities: fuel, parking for car and trailer, toilets, restaurant and children's facilities
Dues: none
Charge: none
Directions: from Glasgow follow A82 then A83 west to west side of Loch Fyne: site is 2 miles south of Furnace
Waters accessed: Loch Fyne and Scottish West Coast

St Catherines - St Catherine's Slip

Type: concrete slipway
Suits: all craft up to 12' LOA
Availability: approx. 4 hours either side HW
Restrictions: site mainly used by hotel visitors
Facilities: petrol, parking for car and trailer, other facilities at nearby hotel
Dues: none
Charge: none
Directions: from Glasgow follow A 82 then A83 west, taking A815 along east shore of Loch Fyne: site is opposite St Catherine's Hotel
Waters accessed: Loch Fyne and Scottish West Coast

Tighnabruaich - Maramarine Ltd, Rhubaan Boatyard
Tel: (0436) 810971 or (0700) 811537

Type: concrete slipway
Suits: all craft
Availability: all states of tide May to October
Restrictions: none known
Facilities: fuel nearby, parking for car and trailer, toilets and boat park on site, chandlery and outboard repairs nearby
Dues: none
Charge: approx. £10.00
Directions: from Glasgow follow A82 then A83 west, taking A815, A886 and A8003 south or ferry to Dunoon A815 then B836 right onto A886 and take A8003 south
Waters accessed: Kyles of Bute, Loch Riddon and Scottish West Coast

Kames, by Tighnabruaich - Tank Landing Slip

Type:	large concrete slipway
Suits:	all craft up to 25' LOA
Availability:	approx. 5 hours either side of HW
Restrictions:	none known
Facilities:	fuel, parking for car and trailer in large car park adjacent, toilets (1 mile), chandlery and repairs nearby
Dues:	none
Charge:	none
Directions:	from Glasgow follow A82 then A83 west, taking A815, A886 and A8003 south or ferry to Dunoon A815 then B836 right onto A886 and take A8003 south, to Tighnabruaich then follow Shore Rd to Kames keeping left and following signs to Ardlamont: site is 1 mile from Kames crossroads

Waters accessed: Kyles of Bute, Loch Riddon and Scottish West Coast

Colintraive - Ferry Stage

Type:	concrete slipway
Suits:	all craft
Availability:	approx. 4 hours either side HW
Restrictions:	ferry must not be obstructed
Facilities:	fuel nearby, limited parking for car and trailer, toilets
Dues:	none
Charge:	none
Directions:	from Glasgow take ferry to Dunoon from Gourock follow A815 then B836 left onto A886 south: site is at ferry crossing to Isle of Bute

Waters accessed: Kyles of Bute, Loch Riddon and Scottish West Coast

Isle of Bute, Rothesay - Outer Harbour Slipway

Type:	concrete slipway
Suits:	all craft
Availability:	approx. 3 hours either side HW
Restrictions:	none known
Facilities:	fuel nearby, parking for car and trailer
Dues:	none
Charge:	none
Directions:	from Glasgow take ferry to Dunoon from Gourock follow A815 then B836 left onto A886 south to Colintraive ferry to Isle of Bute then A886 south to Rothesay, or from Inverclyde via Wemyss Bay ferry

Waters accessed: Kyles of Bute, Loch Riddon and Scottish West Coast

Isle of Bute, Port Bannatyne

Type:	concrete ramp at head of bay
Suits:	all craft up to 25' LOA
Availability:	all states of tide
Restrictions:	none known
Facilities:	fuel nearby, parking for car and trailer
Dues:	none
Charge:	none
Directions:	from Glasgow ferry to Dunoon from Gourock follow A815 then B836 left onto A886 south to Colintraive ferry to Isle of Bute then A886 south, or from Inverclyde via Wemyss Bay ferry
Waters accessed:	Kyles of Bute, Loch Riddon and Scottish West Coast

Isle of Bute, Port Bannatyne - The Port Yard

Type:	concrete slipway with rails
Suits:	all craft
Availability:	approx. 5 hours either side HW
Restrictions:	none known
Facilities:	fuel, parking for car and trailer (c), crane, winch, toilets, chandlery, repairs, moorings
Dues:	none
Charge:	yes
Directions:	from Glasgow ferry to Dunoon from Gourock follow A815 then B836 left onto A886 south to Colintraive ferry to Isle of Bute then A886 south, or from Inverclyde via Wemyss Bay ferry
Waters accessed:	Kyles of Bute, Loch Riddon and Scottish West Coast

Dunoon - Port Riddell Slipway, East Bay

Type:	concrete slipway
Suits:	all craft
Availability:	all states of tide
Restrictions:	none known
Facilities:	fuel nearby, limited parking for car and trailer, toilets nearby
Dues:	none
Charge:	not known
Directions:	from Glasgow by ferry from Gourock
Waters accessed:	Firth of Clyde and Scottish West Coast

Sandbank - Morris & Lorimer (Holy Loch) Ltd
Tel: (0369) 6214

Type:	concrete slipway
Suits:	all craft
Availability:	approx. 1½ hours either side HW by prior arrangement
Restrictions:	none known
Facilities:	no fuel, parking for car and trailer
Dues:	none
Charge:	yes
Directions:	from Glasgow by Gourock ferry to Dunoon and follow A815 north
Waters accessed:	Holy Loch, Firth of Clyde and Scottish West Coast

Clynder - Modern Charters Ltd, Victoria Place, Shore Road
Tel: (0436) 831312/ 684040

Type:	wide concrete slipway
Suits:	dinghies and power boats
Availability:	all states of tide
Restrictions:	12 mph speed limit,
Facilities:	fuel, parking for car and trailer, toilets, chandlery, diving supplies, outboard repairs nearby, cafe, shop, moorings, boat hire and acco-modation
Dues:	none
Charge:	none
Directions:	from Glasgow take A82 onto A814 at Dumbarton to Garelochhead then B833 south to Clynder: site is on west side of loch
Waters accessed:	Gare Loch, Firth of Clyde and Scottish West Coast

Rhu - Rhu Marina
Tel: (0436) 820652

Type:	launching by travel hoist only
Suits:	all craft
Availability:	approx. 3 hours either side HW
Restrictions:	8 knot speed limit: water-skiing prohibited
Facilities:	diesel, parking for car and trailer, toilets, showers, chandlery and engine repairs
Dues:	none
Charge:	yes
Directions:	from Glasgow take A82 onto A814 at Dumbarton to eastern shore of Gare Loch
Waters accessed:	Gare Loch, Firth of Clyde and Scottish West Coast

Helensburgh - Pier

Type:	concrete slipway
Suits:	all craft
Availability:	approx. 3 hours either side HW
Restrictions:	none known
Facilities:	fuel nearby, parking for car and trailer, toilets
Dues:	none
Charge:	yes
Directions:	from Glasgow take A82 onto A814 at Dumbarton and turn left at traffic lights in centre of town: site is adjacent pier

Waters accessed: Gare Loch, Firth of Clyde and Scottish West Coast

Dumbarton - Bridge Street Car Park
Tel: (0389) 27649 / 27663

Type:	concrete slipway
Suits:	all craft up to 9' wide
Availability:	approx. 3 hours either side HW
Restrictions:	water-skiing prohibited
Facilities:	fuel nearby, parking for car and trailer on site, toilets, chandlery and outboard repairs nearby
Dues:	none
Charge:	none
Directions:	from Glasgow follow A82 then A814 into Dumbarton, turn left into High St and right into Bridge St: site is between two road bridges

Waters accessed: River Leven, Firth of Clyde and Scottish West Coast

Loch Lomond - Loch Lomond Marina, Balloch, Loch Lomond
Tel: (0389) 52069

Type:	wooden slipway
Suits:	all craft
Availability:	0900-1900 (summer),0900-1700 (winter) or by arrangement
Restrictions:	none known
Facilities:	petrol (100 yds), diesel, parking for car and trailer (c), toilets, showers, chandlery, tractor and crane all on site
Dues:	none
Charge:	yes
Directions:	from Glasgow follow A82 west: site is at southern end of loch

Waters accessed: Loch Lomond

Renfrew - Clyde River Boatyard
Tel: (041 886) 5974

Type:	concrete slipway
Suits:	all craft up to 40' LOA and 14 tons max
Availability:	approx. 2½ hours either side HW
Restrictions:	speed limit: water-skiing prohibited
Facilities:	diesel on site, petrol (1½ miles), parking for car and trailer (c), toilets, crane and hoist
Dues:	none
Charge:	min charge £40
Directions:	leave M8 at junction 27 and follow signs to Renfrew: access is via Old Kings Inch Rd
Waters accessed:	Firth of Clyde

Glasgow - Strathclyde Country Park, Hamilton

Type:	concrete slipway into 8' water
Suits:	dinghies and powerboats
Availability:	0930 - dusk daily
Restrictions:	water-skiing permitted in designated area: boat drivers must hold Grade 2 licence: all users must report to Booking Office before launching
Facilities:	fuel nearby, parking for car and trailer on site, changing rooms and showers at water sports centre
Dues:	none
Charge:	yes
Directions:	from M74 leave at junction 4 or 5 and follow signs
Waters accessed:	Strathclyde Loch

Port Glasgow - Coronation Park, East Bay
Tel: (0475) 745338 (Recreational Services)

Type:	concrete slipway
Suits:	all craft up to 25' LOA
Availability:	all states of tide except LWS
Restrictions:	none known
Facilities:	fuel (200 yds), parking for car and trailer, toilets, chandlery and yard facilities nearby
Dues:	none
Charge:	none
Directions:	from M8 follow A8 west: access is via tarred road in park
Waters accessed:	River Clyde and Scottish West Coast

Newark - Newark Castle Park
Tel: (0475) 745338 (Recreational Services)

Type:	concrete slipway
Suits:	all craft up to 20' LOA
Availability:	HW only
Restrictions:	none known
Facilities:	fuel, parking for car only
Dues:	none
Charge:	none
Directions:	follow M8 and A8 west from Glasgow, turning off at Newark round-about

Waters accessed: River Clyde and Scottish West Coast

Port Glasgow - Kelburn Riverside Park
Tel: (0475) 745338 (Recreational Services)

Type:	concrete slipway
Suits:	all craft up to 20' LOA
Availability:	approx. 2 hours either side HW
Restrictions:	none known
Facilities:	no fuel, parking for car and trailer, toilets
Dues:	none
Charge:	none
Directions:	follow M8 and A8 west from Glasgow, turning off at Woodhall roundabout

Waters accessed: River Clyde and Scottish West Coast

Greenock - Battery Park
Tel: (0475) 745338(Recreational Services)

Type:	concrete slipway onto shingle
Suits:	all craft up to 25' LOA
Availability:	approx. 2 hours either side HW 0800-1630
Restrictions:	permission to launch required from the Recreational Services Dept
Facilities:	fuel, parking for car and trailer, toilets, chandlery from Gourock
Dues:	none
Charge:	none
Directions:	follow M8 and A8 west from Glasgow to Greenock: access is from Eldon St into park

Waters accessed: River Clyde and Scottish West Coast

Gourock - Cove Road Slipway, Cardwell Bay
Tel: (0475) 745338 (Recreational Services)

Type:	narrow concrete slipway
Suits:	dinghies only
Availability:	approx. 2 hours either side HW
Restrictions:	access is down narrow no through road
Facilities:	fuel, no parking, chandlery from Gourock
Dues:	none
Charge:	none
Directions:	follow M8 then A8 west to Gourock turning right into Cove Rd
Waters accessed:	River Clyde and Scottish West Coast

Gourock - Ashton Slipway
Tel: (0475) 745338 (Recreational Services)

Type:	concrete slipway
Suits:	dinghies only
Availability:	approx. 2 hours either side HW
Restrictions:	narrow entrance to site
Facilities:	no fuel, parking, toilets, chandlery from Gourock
Dues:	none
Charge:	none
Directions:	from Glasgow follow M8 then A8 west to Gourock and signs to Ashton: site is on east side of RGYC
Waters accessed:	River Clyde and Scottish West Coast

Gourock - Maybank Slipway
Tel: (0475) 745338 (Recreational Services)

Type:	concrete slipway
Suits:	dinghies only
Availability:	approx. 2 hours either side HW
Restrictions:	narrow entrance to site
Facilities:	no fuel, parking in main road only, toilets, chandlery from Gourock
Dues:	none
Charge:	none
Directions:	from Glasgow follow M8 then A8 west to Gourock and signs to Ashton
Waters accessed:	River Clyde and Scottish West Coast

Inverkip - Kip Marina
Tel: (0475) 521485 (Holt Leisure Parks Ltd)

Type:	launching by travel hoist only
Suits:	all craft

Availability:	all states of tide during normal working hours
Restrictions:	launching by prior arrangement only
Facilities:	diesel on site, petrol nearby, parking for car and trailer, toilets, showers, sauna, chandlery, diving supplies, engine repairs, launderette, bar and restaurant all on site
Dues:	none
Charge:	approx. £20.00
Directions:	from Glasgow follow M8 then A8 / A78: site is on main road 4 miles south of Greenock
Waters accessed:	Firth of Clyde and Scottish West Coast

Largs - Barrfields Slipway, North Bay

Type:	concrete slipway
Suits:	all craft up to 18' LOA
Availability:	approx. 4 hours either side HW
Restrictions:	slipway must be kept clear at all times for Lifeboat use
Facilities:	fuel nearby, parking for car and trailer nearby, toilets
Dues:	none
Charge:	none
Directions:	from Irvine follow A78 north: access to site is via Shore Rd
Waters accessed:	Firth of Clyde and Scottish West Coast

Largs - Cairney's Quay, South Bay

Type:	concrete slipway
Suits:	all craft which can be manhandled
Availability:	approx. 4 hours either side HW
Restrictions:	no vehicular access, car park has height restriction and for visitors Barrfields slipway is easier: site mainly used by Largs SC
Facilities:	fuel nearby, parking for car and trailer by arrangement with Largs SC (John St), toilets
Dues:	none
Charge:	none
Directions:	from Irvine follow A78 north: access to site is via Shore Rd
Waters accessed:	Firth of Clyde and Scottish West Coast

Largs - Largs Yacht Haven, Irvine Road
Tel: (0475) 675333

Type:	stone slipway
Suits:	all craft up to 25' LOA
Availability:	approx. 3 hours either side HW
Restrictions:	some within marina area: launching may be difficult in strong SW winds
Facilities:	fuel, parking for car and trailer (c), toilets nearby, chandlery, diving supplies, outboard repairs, travel hoist, bar, restaurant and coffee

shop all on site

Dues: none
Charge: none
Directions: from Irvine follow A78 north: site is on left just before railway line off public car park
Waters accessed: Firth of Clyde, Kyles of Bute and Scottish West Coast

Great Cumbrae Island - Scottish National Watersports Training Centre
Tel: (0475) 674666

Type: concrete slipway
Suits: sailing dinghies and trailer-sailers
Availability: approx. 4 hours either side HW by prior arrangement
Restrictions: no powered craft
Facilities: fuel from local garage, parking for car and trailer nearby (c), toilets (400 yds), chandlery in Millport, accomodation
Dues: none
Charge: none
Directions: from Largs by ferry to Great Cumbrae Island: site is on north east corner of island close to ferry terminal
Waters accessed: Firth of Clyde, Kyles of Bute and Scottish West Coast

Great Cumbrae Island - Millport Harbour Slipway

Type: steep concrete slipway
Suits: dinghies only
Availability: approx. 3 hours either side HW
Restrictions: not recommended for general use
Facilities: fuel, parking for car and trailer, chandlery
Dues: none
Charge: none
Directions: from Largs by ferry to Great Cumbrae Island: site is at south end of island
Waters accessed: Firth of Clyde, Kyles of Bute and Scottish West Coast

Saltcoats - Harbour Slipway

Type: stone ramp
Suits: all craft
Availability: approx. 2 hours either side HW
Restrictions: none known
Facilities: petrol, parking for car and trailer, toilets nearby
Dues: none
Charge: none
Directions: from Irvine follow A78 north and turn off to Saltcoats
Waters accessed: Firth of Clyde and Scottish West Coast

Irvine - Harbour Street Slipway
Tel: (0294) 216529 (Irvine Watersports Club)

Type:	concrete slipway
Suits:	all craft up to 18' LOA
Availability:	approx. 3 hours either side HW
Restrictions:	launching by arrangement only
Facilities:	no fuel, parking for car and trailer, toilets nearby
Dues:	none
Charge:	none
Directions:	from Glasgow follow A737 and A736 south: site is in Harbour St close to the Scottish Maritime Museum

Waters accessed: Firth of Clyde and Scottish West Coast

Troon - Troon Marina
Tel: (0292) 315553

Type:	concrete slipway
Suits:	all craft up to 40' LOA
Availability:	all states of tide
Restrictions:	5 knot speed limit in marina
Facilities:	diesel on site, petrol nearby, parking for car and trailer, toilets, showers, sauna, chandlery, diving supplies, boat and engine repairs,bar and restaurant, tractor assistance if required
Dues:	approx. £6.17 (overnight)
Charge:	approx. £7.05
Directions:	from Glasgow follow A77 south then A78 north and follow signs to Troon: access to site is via Harbour Rd

Waters accessed: Firth of Clyde and Scottish West Coast

Ayr - South Harbour Street
Tel: (0292) 281687

Type:	steep concrete slipway with vertical drop at end
Suits:	all craft up to 20' LOA
Availability:	approx. 4 hours either side HW
Restrictions:	5 knot speed limit in harbour: water-skiing permitted offshore
Facilities:	parking for car and trailer nearby, chandlery nearby
Dues:	approx. £5.00
Charge:	none
Directions:	from Glasgow follow A77 south, from town centre drive down south side of harbour

Waters accessed: Ayr Bay, Firth of Clyde and Scottish West Coast

Ayr - Ayr Yacht and Cruising Club, South Harbour Street
Tel: (0292) 267963 (Secretary: Miss E. Hope)

Type:	concrete slipway onto gravel
Suits:	all craft
Availability:	4 hours either side HW for larger craft otherwise all states of tide
Restrictions:	advance notice required, 3rd party indemnity needed water-skiing permitted offshore
Facilities:	fuel in town, parking for car and trailer (c), toilets, showers, chandlery nearby
Dues:	£5.00
Charge:	yes
Directions:	from Glasgow follow A77 south, from town centre drive down south side of harbour
Waters accessed:	Ayr Bay, Firth of Clyde and Scottish West Coast

Girvan - Harbour Slipway
Tel: (0292) 3648

Type:	steep concrete slipway
Suits:	all craft up to 30' LOA
Availability:	approx. 4 hours either side HW by arrangement with Harbour Master
Restrictions:	4 knot speed limit in harbour: narrow access road
Facilities:	fuel nearby, parking for car and trailer nearby, toilets and chandlery nearby
Dues:	approx. £2.00
Charge:	no additional fee
Directions:	from Glasgow follow A77 south, turn off into Newton Place via the Newton Kennedy Bridge
Waters accessed:	Firth of Clyde and Scottish West Coast

Cairnryan - Cairnryan Slipway

Type:	steep concrete slipway onto shingle
Suits:	small craft only
Availability:	all states of tide
Restrictions:	none known
Facilities:	fuel, parking for car and trailer, toilets
Dues:	none
Charge:	none
Directions:	from Stranraer follow A77 north along east shore of Loch Ryan: site is in picnic area just north of Cairnryan
Waters accessed:	Loch Ryan and Scottish West Coast

192

Stranraer - Stranraer Harbour

Type:	concrete slipway
Suits:	all craft
Availability:	approx. 2 hours either side HW
Restrictions:	none known
Facilities:	fuel, parking for car and trailer (c), toilets
Dues:	none
Charge:	none
Directions:	from Dumfries follow A75 west: site is behind Ulster Bus Depot
Waters accessed:	Loch Ryan and Scottish West Coast

Wig Bay - Wig Bay Slip

Type:	concrete slipway
Suits:	all craft
Availability:	all states of tide
Restrictions:	permission to launch should be obtained from Loch Ryan SC
Facilities:	fuel, parking for car and trailer
Dues:	none
Charge:	none
Directions:	from Dumfries follow A75 west then A718 north: site is on west shore Loch Ryan south of Kirkcolm Pt adjacent Loch Ryan SC
Waters accessed:	Loch Ryan and Scottish West Coast

Lady Bay

Type:	concrete slipway onto sand
Suits:	small craft only
Availability:	all states of tide
Restrictions:	site is private but free access is normally granted
Facilities:	no fuel, parking for car and trailer, picnic area
Dues:	none
Charge:	none
Directions:	from Dumfries follow A75 west then A718 north: site is on west shore Loch Ryan
Waters accessed:	Loch Ryan and Scottish West Coast

Portpatrick - Harbour Slipway
Tel: (0776) 810286 (Harbour Master)

Type:	concrete slipway onto shingle and soft sand
Suits:	dinghies only
Availability:	approx. 2 hours either side HW
Restrictions:	consult Harbour Master before use; access is steep, narrow and partially obstructed

Facilities:	fuel, parking for car and trailer, toilets
Dues:	none
Charge:	none
Directions:	from Stranraer follow A716 south then A77 west: site is on south side of Outer Harbour near disused lighthouse
Waters accessed:	North Channel and Scottish West Coast

Port Logan

Type:	concrete slipway onto sand
Suits:	small craft only
Availability:	all states of tide
Restrictions:	none known
Facilities:	no fuel, parking for car and trailer, toilets
Dues:	none
Charge:	none
Directions:	from Stranraer follow A716 south then B7065 to Port Logan
Waters accessed:	Port Logan Bay and Scottish West Coast

Mull of Galloway

Type:	slipway of granite and stone blocks
Suits:	all craft
Availability:	approx. 2 hours either side HW
Restrictions:	site is private but free access is normally given: there are very strong tides in the vicinity of up to 6 knots on spring tides
Facilities:	no fuel, parking for car and trailer
Dues:	none
Charge:	none
Directions:	from Stranraer follow A716 south then B7041 and narrow track to Mull Lighthouse
Waters accessed:	Luce Bay, North Channel and Scottish West Coast

Drummore Harbour

Type:	steep concrete slipway onto hard sand
Suits:	dinghies only
Availability:	approx. 2 hours either side HW
Restrictions:	none known
Facilities:	fuel, parking for car and trailer (c), toilets; Kirkmaiden BC is nearby
Dues:	none
Charge:	none
Directions:	from Stranraer follow A716 south: access is directly from road at bottom of village and opposite Ship Hotel
Waters accessed:	Luce Bay and Scottish West Coast

Sandhead

Type:	launching over soft sand
Suits:	small craft
Availability:	all states of tide
Restrictions:	watch out for nearby bombing range signals
Facilities:	fuel, parking for car and trailer, toilets
Dues:	none
Charge:	none
Directions:	from Stranraer follow A716 south: site is on west shore Luce Bay
Waters accessed:	Luce Bay and Scottish West Coast

Port William

Type:	stone ramp onto gravel beach
Suits:	small craft only
Availability:	approx. 2 hours either side HW
Restrictions:	none known
Facilities:	fuel, parking for car and trailer, toilets
Dues:	none
Charge:	none
Directions:	from Stranraer follow A75 east turning onto A747 at Glenluce: site is on east shore Luce Bay
Waters accessed:	Luce Bay and Scottish West Coast

Isle of Whithorn - Harbour Slipway
Tel: (0988) 500246 (Harbour Master)

Type:	concrete slipway
Suits:	all craft
Availability:	approx. 3 hours either side HW
Restrictions:	consult Harbour Master before use
Facilities:	fuel, parking for car and trailer, winch, toilets, chandlers
Dues:	not known
Charge:	yes
Directions:	from Stranraer follow A75 south east then A747 south
Waters accessed:	Wigtown Bay and Scottish West Coast

Garlieston
Tel: (09886) 259

Type:	launching over shingle
Suits:	all craft
Availability:	approx. 3 hours either side HW
Restrictions:	contact the Harbour Master before launching
Facilities:	fuel, parking for car and trailer, toilets

Dues:	not known
Charge:	yes
Directions:	from Dumfries follow A75 east to Newton Stewart then take A714 south turning onto B7004 1 mile south of Kirkinner: site is on west side of bay in sheltered harbour

Waters accessed: Wigtown Bay and Scottish West Coast

Borgue - Brighouse Bay Holiday Park
Tel: (05577) 267

Type:	concrete slipway
Suits:	all craft
Availability:	most states of tide
Restrictions:	obtain permission from park reception prior to launching
Facilities:	no fuel, parking for car and trailer, toilets, shop, leisure club, golf course and indoor swimming pool all on site
Dues:	included in fee
Charge:	approx. £6.00
Directions:	from Kirkcudbright follow A755 west for ½ mile, turning left onto B727 signposted Borgue: after 4 miles take left turning signposted Brighouse Bay: site is on right after 2 miles

Waters accessed: Dee Estuary and North Irish Sea

Kirkcudbright - Harbour Slipway
Tel: (0557) 331135 (Harbour Master)

Type:	uneven stone slipway onto shingle
Suits:	all craft up to 18' LOA
Availability:	approx. 2 hours either side HW
Restrictions:	speed limit: no water-skiing: contact the Harbour Master prior to launching
Facilities:	fuel from garage, parking for car and trailer in car park, toilets, chandlery, diving supplies, outboard repairs and all town facilities nearby
Dues:	approx. £3.06
Charge:	none
Directions:	from Dumfries follow A75 west turning left onto A711: site is on east shore of estuary

Waters accessed: Dee Estuary and North Irish Sea

Kirkcudbright - Gibb Hill Sawmill

Type: concrete slipway
Suits: all craft
Availability: approx. 3-4 hours either side HW
Restrictions: none known
Facilities: fuel nearby, limited parking for car and trailer
Dues: none
Charge: yes
Directions: from Dumfries follow A75 west, turning south onto A711 and crossing to west shore of estuary: site is adjacent Gibb Hill Sawmill
Waters accessed: Dee Estuary and North Irish Sea

Kippford

Type: concrete slipway onto shingle
Suits: all craft up to 18' LOA
Availability: approx. 2 hours either side HW
Restrictions: none known
Facilities: fuel, parking for car and trailer, toilets, chandlery
Dues: none
Charge: none
Directions: from Dumfries follow A711 to Dalbeattie then A710 south for 4 miles turning right onto minor road
Waters accessed: Solway Firth and North Irish Sea

Parton - Galloway Sailing Centre (Loch Ken)
Tel: (06442) 626

Type: concrete slipway
Suits: sailing craft only up to 28' LOA
Availability: at all times (non tidal) Easter to end Oct
Restrictions: speed limit: no ski boats or pwc; 3rd party insurance certificate required
Facilities: fuel (3 miles), parking for car and trailer, toilets, chandlery, outboard repairs nearby, showers, changing rooms, catering (1000 to 1730)
Dues: none
Charge: approx. £5.00
Directions: from Dumfries follow A75 to Castle Douglas then north onto A713: site is 10 miles north
Waters accessed: Loch Ken only

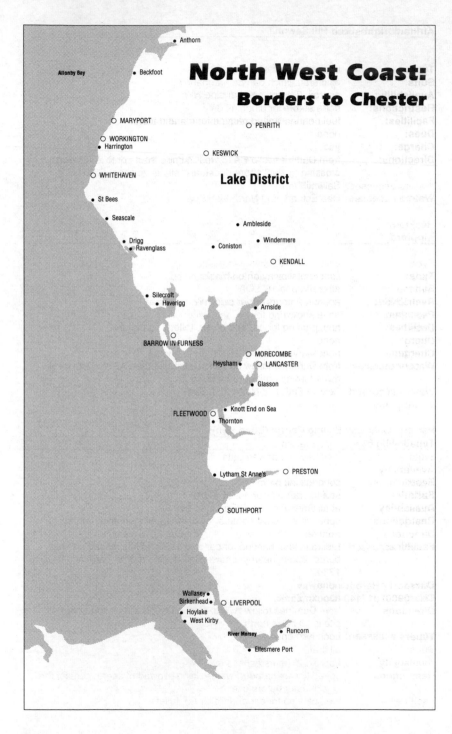

North West Coast:
Borders to Chester

Anthorn

Allonby Bay

Beckfoot

○ MARYPORT

○ WORKINGTON
• Harrington

○ PENRITH

• KESWICK

○ WHITEHAVEN

Lake District

• St Bees

• Seascale

• Ambleside

• Drigg
• Ravenglass

• Coniston

• Windermere

○ KENDALL

• Silecroft
• Haverigg

• Arnside

○ BARROW IN FURNESS

○ MORECOMBE

Heysham • ○ LANCASTER

• Glasson

FLEETWOOD ○ • Knott End on Sea
• Thornton

• Lytham St Anne's

○ PRESTON

○ SOUTHPORT

Wallasey •
Birkenhead • ○ LIVERPOOL
• Hoylake
• West Kirby

River Mersey

• Runcorn

• Ellesmere Port

Anthorn - Foreshore

Type:	launching over shingle foreshore
Suits:	light craft which can be manhandled
Availability:	approx. 2 hours either side HW
Restrictions:	site suitable for dinghies only
Facilities:	fuel from garage, parking for car and trailer
Dues:	none
Charge:	none
Directions:	from Carlisle follow B5307 to Kirkbride then minor roads north for 4 miles

Waters accessed: Solway Firth

Beckfoot

Type:	launching over shingle foreshore
Suits:	light craft which can be manhandled
Availability:	near HW
Restrictions:	water-skiing permitted but site is exposed
Facilities:	no fuel, parking for car and trailer
Dues:	none
Charge:	none
Directions:	from Maryport follow B5300 north approx 10 miles

Waters accessed: Solway Firth

Allonby Bay

Type:	concrete slipway
Suits:	dinghies and powerboats
Availability:	all states of tide
Restrictions:	water-skiing permitted but site is exposed
Facilities:	no fuel, parking for car and trailer
Dues:	none
Charge:	none
Directions:	from Maryport follow B5300 north approx 5 miles

Waters accessed: Solway Firth

Maryport - Harbour Slipway
Tel: (0900) 817440 (Dockmaster)

Type:	concrete slipway
Suits:	all craft
Availability:	approx. 2½ hours either side HW
Restrictions:	speed limit in harbour: water-skiing allowed offshore; contact the Dockmaster before use
Facilities:	fuel, parking for car and trailer (c), toilets

Dues: not known
Charge: yes
Directions: from Carlisle follow A596 south; site is behind coastguard station
Waters accessed: Solway Firth

Workington - Tidal Dock
Tel: (06973) 43293 (Vanguard Sailing Club)

Type: concrete slipway
Suits: all craft up to 35' LOA
Availability: approx. 2½ hours either side HW, or later for small craft
Restrictions: slow speed in harbour: water-skiing allowed to seaward of Lifeboat mooring
Facilities: fuel in town (1 mile), parking for car and trailer; associate membership of club with use of facilities available
Dues: not known
Charge: yes
Directions: from Carlisle follow A596 south; site is on south side of dock just seaward of railway bridge
Waters accessed: Solway Firth

Harrington - Harbour Slipway
Tel: (0946) 830600 (Harrington Sailing & Fishing Club)

Type: concrete slipway
Suits: trailer-sailers
Availability: approx. 2 hours either side HW
Restrictions: permission to use slipway must be obtained in advance; this is a small port, giving access to exposed open sea conditions, which is not suitable for dinghies and inflatables
Facilities: fuel, parking for car and trailer, toilets
Dues: not known
Charge: yes
Directions: from Workington follow A597 south for approx. 3 miles
Waters accessed: Solway Firth

Whitehaven - Lime Tongue Slipway
Tel: (0946) 2435 (Harbour Office, Duke Street)

Type: steep stone slipway
Suits: all craft up to 18' LOA
Availability: approx 2 hours either side HW
Restrictions: 5 mph speed limit in harbour: water-skiing allowed offshore; this is a busy fishing harbour; prior permission to use slipway must be obtained from the Harbour Master
Facilities: fuel from Donnans Fish Merchant, Sugar Tongue or from town, parking for car and trailer, toilets in Market Place

Dues:	not known
Charge:	none
Directions:	from town centre follow A595 north turning off at Looe Rd: site is between Lime Tongue and Sugar Tongue Quays
Waters accessed:	Solway Firth

St Bees - Beach

Type:	concrete slipway
Suits:	small craft only
Availability:	approx. 2 hours either side HW
Restrictions:	site is very exposed in onshore winds
Facilities:	no fuel, parking for car and trailer, no toilets
Dues:	none
Charge:	none
Directions:	from Whitehaven follow B5345 south and local roads to beach
Waters accessed:	Irish Sea

Seascale - Beach

Type:	launching over shingle beach
Suits:	light craft
Availability:	all states of tide in offshore winds only
Restrictions:	site is very exposed in onshore winds
Facilities:	no fuel, parking for car and trailer
Dues:	none
Charge:	none
Directions:	from Whitehaven follow A595 south turning onto B5344
Waters accessed:	Irish Sea

Drigg - Beach

Type:	launching over pebble and sand beach
Suits:	light craft
Availability:	HW in offshore winds only
Restrictions:	site is very exposed and dangerous in onshore winds
Facilities:	no fuel, parking for car and trailer
Dues:	none
Charge:	none
Directions:	from Whitehaven follow A595 south to Holmrook and turn onto B5344; follow minor roads over railway line to shore (approx. 1 mile)
Waters accessed:	Irish Sea

Ravenglass

Type:	concrete ramp or over beaches into harbour
Suits:	all craft
Availability:	approx. 2 hours either side HW
Restrictions:	harbour is very exposed and dangerous in onshore winds and currents within the harbour are very strong
Facilities:	fuel from garage, parking for car and trailer nearby, pub and shop
Dues:	none
Charge:	none
Directions:	follow A595 south turning off into village; site is at end of street into natural harbour formed by the rivers Irt, Mite and Esk
Waters accessed:	Irish Sea

Silecroft - Beach

Type:	launching over pebble and sand beach
Suits:	small craft
Availability:	near HW in offshore winds only
Restrictions:	site is very exposed and dangerous in onshore winds
Facilities:	no fuel, parking for car and trailer
Dues:	none
Charge:	none
Directions:	from Whitehaven follow A595 south turning onto the minor road which leads off at the junction of A595 and A5093
Waters accessed:	Irish Sea

Haverigg

Type:	concrete slipway
Suits:	small craft only
Availability:	approx. 2½ hours either side HW
Restrictions:	not known
Facilities:	no fuel, parking for car and trailer
Dues:	none
Charge:	none
Directions:	from Whitehaven follow A595 and A5093 south to Millom turning onto minor roads to Haverigg: site is at mouth of Duddon Estuary close to Rugby Union Club
Waters accessed:	Duddon Estuary and Irish Sea

Barrow-in-Furness - The Promenade, Isle of Walney

Type:	wide stone slipway
Suits:	all craft
Availability:	at all states of tide
Restrictions:	none
Facilities:	fuel from garage (1 mile), parking for car and trailer nearby
Dues:	none
Charge:	none
Directions:	from Barrow in Furness follow A590 to the island; site is opposite the Ferry Inn
Waters accessed:	Irish Sea

Arnside - Promenade

Type:	concrete slipway onto soft mud
Suits:	all craft
Availability:	all states of tide
Restrictions:	beware of strong tide and the "bore" in the Kent Estuary
Facilities:	fuel, parking for car and trailer (c), toilets in village; visitors are welcome at the Arnside SC on promontory at end of Promenade
Dues:	none
Charge:	none
Directions:	leave M6 at junction 36 taking A590 north and then left onto B5282: site is adjacent Crossfields Boatyard at seaward end of Promenade
Waters accessed:	Kent Estuary, Morecambe Bay and Irish Sea

Morecambe - Promenade
Tel: (0524) 582808

Type:	4 concrete slipways
Suits:	all craft
Availability:	approx. 3 hours either side HW
Restrictions:	8 mph speed limit inshore: water-skiing permitted offshore; obtain permit for vehicular access to promenade
Facilities:	fuel nearby, parking for car in Marine Drive or nearby car parks (c), trailers may be left near slipways for up to 24 hrs, toilets and other facilities nearby
Dues:	none
Charge:	none
Directions:	leave M6 at junction 33/34 through Lancaster or junction 35 via Carnforth: sites are located on 5 mile stretch of Promenade
Waters accessed:	Morecambe Bay and Irish Sea

Glasson Dock - Glasson Basin Yacht Co
Tel: (0524) 751491

Type:	concrete slipway into locked basin
Suits:	all craft
Availability:	by prior arrangement only
Restrictions:	24 hrs notice required to lock out into Glasson Dock, gates can be opened 1 hour before HW: access to Lancaster Canal is via locks which take boats up to 72' LOA 14' wide and 4' draught
Facilities:	fuel, parking for car and trailer (c), toilets, showers, chandlery, crane, winch and other boatyard facilities
Dues:	BW licence required if entering canal network
Charge:	yes
Directions:	leave M6 at junction 34 taking A588 south and turning onto B5290 at Conder Green
Waters accessed:	Lancaster Canal and River Lune Estuary via Glasson Dock

Glasson Dock - Glasson SC, Fishnet Place

Type:	concrete slipway
Suits:	all craft up to 20' LOA
Availability:	approx. 2 hours either side HW by prior arrangement
Restrictions:	dinghy racing has priority over all other uses
Facilities:	fuel nearby, parking for car and trailer and toilets on site, other facilities nearby
Dues:	none
Charge:	approx. £10
Directions:	leave M6 at junction 34 taking A588 south and turning onto B5290 at Conder Green: at Glasson Dock proceed along west Quay and through Industrial Site to club
Waters accessed:	River Lune Estuary and Irish Sea

Knott-End-on-Sea - Knott End Ferry Stage

Type:	concrete slipway
Suits:	all craft
Availability:	at all states of tide but 2 hours either side HW is best
Restrictions:	ferries must not be obstructed
Facilities:	no fuel, parking for car and trailer, no toilets
Dues:	not known
Charge:	yes
Directions:	leave M6 at junction 34 taking A588 south and turning onto B5270 to Preesall and Knott-End-on-Sea: site is at ferry terminal opposite Fleetwood
Waters accessed:	River Wyre and Irish Sea

Thornton - Stanah Car Park

Type:	fairly steep concrete slipway (1:10)
Suits:	all craft up to 25' LOA
Availability:	approx. 2 hours either side HW
Restrictions:	none known
Facilities:	no fuel, parking for car and trailer, toilets
Dues:	none known
Charge:	none
Directions:	leave M55 at junction 3 taking A585 towards Fleetwood, turning right into Skippool Rd then right again into River Rd
Waters accessed:	River Wyre and Irish Sea

Blackpool - Little Bispham, Princes Way
Tel: (0253) 21623

Type:	concrete ramp onto sand and shingle beach
Suits:	small craft
Availability:	all states of tide if suitable vehicle is used
Restrictions:	8 knot speed limit within 200m LWS mark: water-skiing permitted in designated areas
Facilities:	no fuel, parking for car and trailer nearby(c), toilets nearby
Dues:	none
Charge:	none
Directions:	from M55 follow signs to seafront: from Blackpool Tower, continue along the Promenade northwards for approx. 3½ miles, turning left for site at Little Bispham tramstop
Waters accessed:	Irish Sea

Blackpool - Starr Gate
Tel: (0253) 21623

Type:	concrete ramp onto sand and shingle beach
Suits:	small craft
Availability:	all states of tide if suitable vehicle is used
Restrictions:	8 knot speed limit within 200m LWS mark: water-skiing permitted in designated areas
Facilities:	no fuel, parking for car and trailer on site (c), toilets on site
Dues:	none
Charge:	none
Directions:	from M55 follow signs to seafront: from Blackpool Tower, continue along the Promenade southwards for approx. 3 miles and site is on right
Waters accessed:	Irish Sea

Lytham St Anne's - Central Beach Slipway

Type:	concrete slipway
Suits:	all craft
Availability:	approx. 2-3 hours either side HW
Restrictions:	8 knot speed limit within 200m LWS mark: water-skiing permitted in designated areas
Facilities:	fuel nearby, parking for car and trailer (c), toilets. chandlery and repairs from Lytham Boat Centre
Dues:	none
Charge:	none
Directions:	leave M55 at junction 4 taking A583 south then minor roads, following signs to seafront
Waters accessed:	Ribble Estuary and Irish Sea

Lytham St Annes - Lytham Boat Centre, Dock Road
Tel: (0253) 730759

Type:	concrete slipway
Suits:	all craft
Availability:	approx. 2 hours either side HW
Restrictions:	speed limit; water-skiing permitted in river
Facilities:	fuel, parking for car and trailer (c), toilets, showers, chandlery and other boatyard facilities
Dues:	none
Charge:	yes
Directions:	from M55 turn off at junction 4 and take A583 south then minor roads: access to site is via Dock Rd
Waters accessed:	Ribble Estuary and Irish Sea

Preston - Douglas Boatyard, Becconsall Lane, Hesketh Bank
Tel: (0772) 812462

Type:	concrete slipway
Suits:	mainly larger sailing and motor cruisers between 20'-50' LOA
Availability:	approx. 2 hours either side of HW by prior arrangement
Restrictions:	speed limit near moorings
Facilities:	diesel on site, petrol nearby, parking for car and trailer, toilets, chandlery, moorings and yard services all on site
Dues:	on application
Charge:	on application
Directions:	from Preston take A59 south to Tarleton turning onto road towards Hesketh Bank: take first right after Becconsall Hotel into Becconsall Lane
Waters accessed:	Rivers Douglas and Ribble and the Irish Sea

Liverpool - Salthouse Slipway, Salthouse Dock
Tel: (051 236) 6090 (Harbour Master)

Type:	steep concrete slipway (1:8) into 5' water
Suits:	small craft
Availability:	0900-sunset by prior arrangement
Restrictions:	speed limit: no water-skiing; site gives access to approx. 65 acres of water but with restricted headroom under bridges
Facilities:	fuel nearby, parking for car and trailer on site (c), toilets, chandlery, watersports centre, shops and restaurants all available nearby
Dues:	approx. £4.00
Charge:	no additional fee charged
Directions:	from M62 follow signs to Liverpool City Centre / Pier Head / Albert Dock, turning off Inner Ring Road to Albert Dock
Waters accessed:	Liverpool South Docks: access to River Mersey possible by prior arrangement

Liverpool - Liverpool Marina, Coburg Dock, Sefton St
Tel: (051 236) 6090 (Harbour Master)

Type:	large concrete slipway into locked basin
Suits:	all craft
Availability:	approx. 2½ hours either side HW during normal working hours
Restrictions:	access to tidal river through Brunswick Dock lock gates which open approx. 2½ hours either side HW (end March-end Oct) or by arrangement
Facilities:	diesel on site, petrol nearby, parking for car and trailer, toilets, showers, no chandlery but other marina facilities on site
Dues:	licence required
Charge:	yes
Directions:	from Inner Ring Rd follow signs to Albert Dock Complex: marina is in Coburg Dock off Sefton St to south of Albert Dock
Waters accessed:	dock complex and River Mersey via lock

New Brighton - Victoria Road, South Slipway
Tel: (051 647) 2366

Type:	concrete slipway onto hard sand
Suits:	all craft
Availability:	at all states of tide except 1 hour either side LWS
Restrictions:	8 knot speed limit inshore on N. Wirral coast: this is a major shipping river with strong currents, pleasure craft must obey Port Regulations; site is very busy at weekends in summer
Facilities:	fuel from nearby garage, parking for car and trailer nearby (with permit), toilets on Promenade
Dues:	none
Charge:	none, but permit is required for vehicles driving on foreshore -

Directions: leave M53 at junction 1 and follow signs to seafront: site lies at the eastern end of the Promenade

Waters accessed: Mersey Estuary

Hoylake - Dove Point Slipway, Meols
Tel: (051 647) 2366

Type:	concrete slipway onto hard sand
Suits:	small shallow-draught craft
Availability:	approx. 2 hours either side HW
Restrictions:	8 knot speed limit inshore on N. Wirral coast
Facilities:	fuel from nearby garage, parking for car on Promenade and for trailer by slipway, toilets
Dues:	none
Charge:	none, but permit is required for vehicles launching - obtainable from Dept. of Leisure Services and Tourism, Wirral MBC, Westminster House, Hamilton St, Birkenhead, Wirral
Directions:	leave M53 at junction 2 taking A551/A553: site is at the eastern end of the Meols Promenade by the Coastguard Office

Waters accessed: Mersey Estuary and Irish Sea

West Kirby - Sandy Lane Slipway (West Kirby Marine Lake)
Tel: (051 647) 2366

Type:	concrete slipway
Suits:	all craft
Availability:	approx. 2½ hours either side HW
Restrictions:	none
Facilities:	fuel in W. Kirby, parking for car and trailer on Promenade, toilets and chandlery nearby
Dues:	none
Charge:	none but permit is required - obtainable from Dept. of Leisure Services and Tourism, Wirral MBC, Westminster House, Hamilton St, Birkenhead, Wirral
Directions:	leave M53 at junction 2 following A551/A553: site is at southern end of the West Kirby Marine Lake which is well signposted

Waters accessed: Dee Estuary and Irish Sea

LAKE DISTRICT

Coniston - Coniston Boating Centre, Lake Road
Tel: (05394) 41366

Type:	concrete slipway
Suits:	all craft up to 26' LOA
Availability:	0900-1730
Restrictions:	10 mph speed limit: narrow bridge on approach road to site
Facilities:	fuel nearby, parking for car and trailer, toilets, cafe, picnic area, boat park; hand winch and 4-wheel drive assistance available (c)
Dues:	none
Charge:	approx. £6.00
Directions:	from M6 turn off at junction 36 and take A590/A591 to Windermere, continuing to Ambleside and turning onto A593 to Coniston: turn left by garage into Lake Rd
Waters accessed:	Coniston Water

Coniston - Monk Coniston Car Park
Tel: (05394) 46601 (Visitor Services)

Type:	launching over gravel shore
Suits:	small non-powered craft only
Availability:	during daylight hours
Restrictions:	powered craft prohibited
Facilities:	fuel in Coniston, parking for car and trailer on site (c), toilets on site
Dues:	none
Charge:	none
Directions:	leave M6 at junction 36 and take A590/A591 to Windermere, continuing to Ambleside and turning onto A593 to Coniston: turn left onto B5285 following road round north shore of lake; site is reached through car park
Waters accessed:	Coniston Water

Coniston - Brown Howe Car Park
Tel: (05394) 46601 (Visitor Services)

Type:	launching over gravel shore
Suits:	small non-powered craft only
Availability:	during daylight hours
Restrictions:	powered craft prohibited
Facilities:	fuel nearby, parking for car and trailer on site (c), toilets on site
Dues:	none
Charge:	none
Directions:	leave M6 at junction 36 and take A590/A591 to Windermere, continuing to Ambleside; turn onto A593 to south of Coniston taking the A5084 to SW corner of lake: site is reached through car park
Waters accessed:	Coniston Water

Keswick - Keswick-on-Derwentwater Launch Co Ltd
Tel: (07687) 72263

Type:	launching over shingle shore
Suits:	small craft only
Availability:	0900-2130 (Mar-Nov)
Restrictions:	10 mph speed limit
Facilities:	no fuel, parking for car and trailer, toilets
Dues:	none
Charge:	approx. £3.50
Directions:	leave M6 at junction 40 and follow A66 west to Keswick: site is on W shore of lake

Waters accessed: Derwentwater

Portinscale - Derwentwater Marina
Tel: (07687) 72912

Type:	2 concrete ramps into 3' water
Suits:	all craft up to 25' LOA and 10' wide
Availability:	during daylight hours
Restrictions:	10 mph speed limit
Facilities:	fuel from Keswick, parking for car and trailer, toilets and showers, chandlery, outboard repairs and restaurant
Dues:	none
Charge:	approx. £6.00
Directions:	leave M6 at junction 40 following A66 west to Keswick and continuing on to Portinscale; site is ½ mile after village

Waters accessed: Derwentwater

Portinscale - Nichol End Marine
Tel: (07687) 73082

Type:	steel slipway into 4' water
Suits:	all craft up to 25' LOA
Availability:	at all times, preferably by prior arrangement
Restrictions:	10 mph speed limit
Facilities:	petrol, parking for car and trailer, toilets, chandlery, outboard repairs, boat repairs and refreshments all on site
Dues:	none
Charge:	approx. £6.50 (inc. overnight mooring if required)
Directions:	leave M6 at junction 40 following A66 west to Keswick and continuing on to Portinscale; turn left ½ mile after village after marina

Waters accessed: Derwentwater

Derwentwater - Kettlewell Car Park (National Trust)

Type: launching over gravel shore
Suits: small non-powered craft only
Availability: during daylight hours
Restrictions: 10 mph speed limit: powered craft prohibited
Facilities: limited parking for car and trailer on site (c), toilets nearby
Dues: none
Charge: none
Directions: leave M6 at junction 40 and follow A66 west to Keswick; turn left onto Borrowdale road (B5289) and follow for approx. 2½ miles: site is ½ mile north of Lodore
Waters accessed: Derwentwater

Ullswater - Glencoyne Bay

Type: launching over gravel shore
Suits: small non-powered craft only
Availability: during daylight hours
Restrictions: 10 mph speed limit: powered craft prohibited
Facilities: limited parking for car and trailer on site
Dues: none
Charge: none
Directions: leave M6 at junction 40 and follow A66 west turning left onto A592 and following road to Glencoyne: site is close to bridge
Waters accessed: Ullswater

Ullswater - Howtown

Type: launching over gravel shore
Suits: craft up to 20' LOA
Availability: during daylight hours
Restrictions: 10 mph speed limit: narrow access road
Facilities: limited parking for car and trailer on site
Dues: none
Charge: none
Directions: leave M6 at junction 40 and follow A66 west turning left onto A592; at top of lake turn left onto B5320 to Pooley Bridge and follow minor road south for 3 miles
Waters accessed: Ullswater

Ullswater - The Spit, Glenridding (Glenridding Sailing School)
Tel: (07684) 86601/82541

Type:	launching over shingle beach
Suits:	sailing dinghies and windsurfers
Availability:	1000-1700 daily (end Mar-Oct) by prior arrangement
Restrictions:	all launchers must report to office on arrival: personal buoyancy must be worn: launching is at site owners' discretion
Facilities:	parking for car and trailer on site, toilets nearby, safety boats
Dues:	none
Charge:	approx. £4.00
Directions:	leave M6 at junction 40 and follow A66 west, turning left onto A592 and following road to Glenridding: access to site is via drive between the Ullswater and Glenridding Hotels and opposite the entrance to National Park Car Park

Waters accessed: Ullswater

Bowness-on-Windermere - Shepherd's Boatyard, Bowness Bay
Tel: (05394) 45395

Type:	concrete slipway
Suits:	powered craft and trailer-sailers
Availability:	0900-1700
Restrictions:	6 mph speed limit in certain areas: all powered craft must be registered; towed inflatables prohibited
Facilities:	fuel, parking for car and trailer, chandlery and outboard repairs all available on site
Dues:	annual registration fee approx £5 pa (less than 10hp) or £25 pa (10-80hp)
Charge:	approx. £9.00
Directions:	leave M6 at junction 36 and take A590/A591 to Windermere; turn left onto A592 to Bowness

Waters accessed: Lake Windermere

Bowness-on-Windermere - Ferry Nab
Tel: (05394) 42753 (Lake Warden's Office)

Type:	concrete slipway into 4' water: tractor assistance available
Suits:	craft up to 35' LOA and 11 tons max. incl. trailer and vehicle
Availability:	daily 0900-1700 in winter, 0800-2200 in summer
Restrictions:	6 mph speed limit in certain areas: all powered craft must be registered at slipway office; towed inflatables prohibited
Facilities:	fuel, parking for car and trailer on site (c), showers, boat park on site, toilets in car park; chandlery and outboard repairs available from boatyards nearby
Dues:	annual registration fee approx £5 pa (less than 10hp) or £25 pa (10-80hp)
Charge:	approx. £5.00 if non-motorised and £10.00 if motorised

Directions: leave M6 at junction 36 and take A590/A591 to roundabout at N. end of Kendal bypass; take either the B5284 signposted Hawkshead via ferry or continue to Windermere and turn left onto A592 to Bowness

Waters accessed: Lake Windermere

Ambleside - Waterhead
Tel: (05394) 42753 (Lake Warden's Office)

Type:	launching over shingle beach
Suits:	craft up to 20' LOA and 5hp engine capacity
Availability:	during daylight hours
Restrictions:	6 mph speed limit in certain areas; all powered craft must be registered; towed inflatables prohibited
Facilities:	fuel from Waterhead Marine, parking for car and trailer (c), toilets
Dues:	annual registration fee approx £5 pa (less than 10hp) or £25 pa (10-80hp)
Charge	yes
Directions:	from M6 turn off at junction 36 and take A590/A591 to Windermere, continuing to Ambleside; turn onto A591 south

Waters accessed: Lake Windermere

Ambleside - Low Wray Campsite
Tel: (05394) 32810 (National Trust Warden)

Type:	launching over gravel shore
Suits:	small non-powered craft only
Availability:	during daylight hours
Restrictions:	powered craft prohibited: facility generally only available for use by campers at site; non-campers should telephone first
Facilities:	parking for car and trailer on site, toilets, other facilities from boatyards nearby
Dues	included in launching fee
Charge	yes
Directions:	leave M6 at junction 36 and take A590/A591 to Windermere, continuing to Ambleside; turn onto B5286 and follow signs: site is 3 miles south of Ambleside

Waters accessed: Lake Windermere

Harrowslack
Tel: (05394) 44746 (National Trust Warden)

Type:	launching over gravel shore
Suits:	small non-powered craft only
Availability:	during daylight hours
Restrictions:	powered craft prohibited: permit must be obtained from N.T. Warden

Facilities:	parking for car and trailer on site
Dues	included in launching fee
Charge	approx. £1.00
Directions:	leave M6 at junction 36 and take A590/A591 to Windermere, continuing to Ambleside; turn onto B5286 and then follow B5285 from Hawkshead

Waters accessed: Lake Windermere

Newby Bridge - Fell Foot Park
Tel: (05395) 31273 (Manager)

Type:	launching over gravel shore
Suits:	small sailing craft and small powered craft up to 5 hp
Availability:	1000-1700; gates locked at 2000
Restrictions:	6 mph speed limit in certain areas: open speedboats over 5hp and pwc prohibited: cruisers with engines but with separate lockable living accomodation are allowed
Facilities:	fuel from garage in Newby Bridge (1½ miles), parking for car and trailer (c), toilets and cafe available on site: jetty space available by prior arrangement
Dues	included in launching fee
Charge	approx. £13.00 incl. parking
Directions:	from M6 turn off at junction 36 and take A590 to southern end of lake: please use north entrance to park

Waters accessed: Lake Windermere

Wales

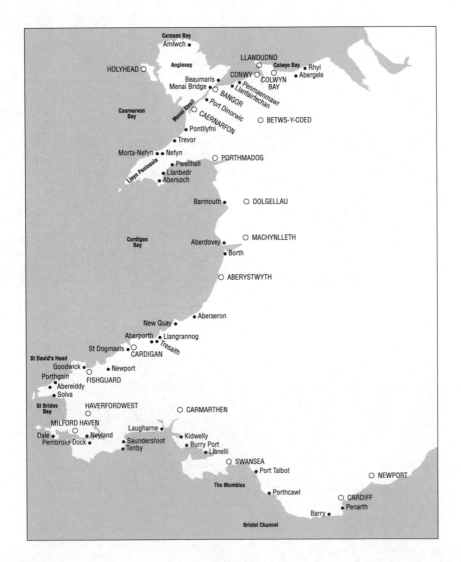

Rhyl - Rhyl Yacht Club, Foryd Harbour

Type:	concrete slipway
Suits:	all craft
Availability:	approx. 2 hours either side HW by prior arrangement
Restrictions:	5 mph speed limit in harbour: water-skiing permitted outside harbour
Facilities:	fuel from garage, parking for car and trailer (c), toilets in clubhouse
Dues:	none
Charge:	yes
Directions:	from Chester follow A55 west, turn onto A525 to Rhyl; in town centre turn left onto A548; site is on south side of bridge
Waters accessed:	Kinmel Bay, Liverpool Bay and Irish Sea

Kinmel Bay - Seafront

Type:	short concrete ramp onto soft sandy beach
Suits:	small craft which can be manhandled
Availability:	all states of tide
Restrictions:	speed limit within 200m of shore: water-skiing permitted outside limit; site faces NW and is exposed
Facilities:	fuel (250yds), parking for car and trailer, toilets (200yds), chandlers nearby
Dues:	none
Charge:	none
Directions:	from Chester follow A55 west to Abergele, turning right onto A548: access is via St Asaph Ave and across pedestrian promenade
Waters accessed:	Kinmel Bay, Liverpool Bay and Irish Sea

Abergele - Pensarn Beach

Type:	launching across shingle bank onto sand
Suits:	small craft which can be manhandled
Availability:	near HW only
Restrictions:	speed limit within 200m of shore with access lane for water-skiing; site is difficult and exposed
Facilities:	fuel (250yds), parking for car and trailer, toilets (100yds), chandlers nearby
Dues:	none
Charge:	none
Directions:	from Chester follow A55 west to Abergele and then signs to Pensarn seafront
Waters accessed:	Liverpool Bay and Irish Sea

Llanddulas - Llanddulas Beach

Type: short concrete ramp onto shingle and sand
Suits: small craft which can be manhandled
Availability: all states of tide
Restrictions: speed limit within 200m of shore: water-skiing permitted outside limit; site faces N and is difficult and exposed
Facilities: fuel, parking for car and trailer, toilets
Dues: none
Charge: none
Directions: from Chester follow A55 west
Waters accessed: Colwyn Bay

Old Colwyn - Old Colwyn Slipway

Type: short concrete ramp onto shingle and sand
Suits: small craft which can be manhandled
Availability: near HW only
Restrictions: speed limit within 200m of shore: water-skiing permitted outside limit; site is difficult and exposed and level of beach liable to change
Facilities: fuel (1 mile), parking for car and trailer on promenade (50yds), toilets nearby
Dues: none
Charge: none
Directions: from Chester follow A55 west: access is via promenade
Waters accessed: Colwyn Bay

Colwyn Bay - Dingle Slipway

Type: steep concrete ramp onto sand
Suits: small craft which can be manhandled
Availability: near HW only
Restrictions: speed limit within 200m of sea wall: water-skiing permitted outside limit but there is no provision for skiing from the shore; site is very close to groyne and exposed
Facilities: fuel (1 mile), parking for car and trailer on promenade, toilets (20yds)
Dues: none
Charge: none
Directions: from Chester follow A55 west: access is from pedestrian promenade
Waters accessed: Colwyn Bay

Rhos-on-Sea - Aberhod Slipway

Type:	concrete slipway onto sand
Suits:	small craft which can be manhandled
Availability:	all states of tide but best 4 hours either side HW
Restrictions:	speed limit within 200m of shore with access lane for water-skiing ; site is sheltered and used by local SC
Facilities:	fuel (200yds), parking for car and trailer on promenade, toilets (100yds)
Dues:	none known
Charge:	none
Directions:	from Chester follow A55 west, turning onto B5115 and minor roads: access is via promenade

Waters accessed: Colwyn Bay

Conwy Morfa - Beacons Recreational Area
Tel: (0492) 596253 (Harbour Master)

Type:	steep concrete slipway
Suits:	all craft
Availability:	approx. 3 hours either side HW
Restrictions:	5 mph speed limit inshore: water-skiing permitted outside harbour
Facilities:	fuel nearby, parking for car and trailer and refreshments on site, toilets, chandlery and outboard repairs nearby
Dues:	none
Charge:	approx. £6.50
Directions:	from Chester follow A55 west through the Conwy Tunnel, taking the exit immediately after the tunnel and following signs to Beacons

Waters accessed: Conwy Bay and Irish Sea

Penmaenmawr - New Promenade
Tel: (0492) 596253 (Harbour Master)

Type:	concrete slipway onto hard sand
Suits:	small craft
Availability:	all states of tide over beach
Restrictions:	none
Facilities:	fuel nearby, parking for car and trailer and toilets on site
Dues:	none
Charge:	yes
Directions:	from Conwy follow A55 expressway and signs to Penmaenmawr: access is via road over expressway at W end of Promenade

Waters accessed: Conwy Bay, Menai Straits and Irish Sea

Llanfairfechan - Llanfairfechan Sailing Club, The Promenade
Tel: (0248) 680301

Type:	concrete slipway
Suits:	small craft
Availability:	all states of tide over beach
Restrictions:	none
Facilities:	no fuel, parking for car and trailer (c), toilets in clubhouse,dinghy park, temporary membership available to visitors
Dues:	none
Charge:	yes
Directions:	from Conwy follow A55 expressway and signs to Llanfairfechan
Waters accessed:	Conwy Bay, Menai Straits and Irish Sea

Bangor - A M Dickie & Sons, Garth Road
Tel: (0248) 352775

Type:	concrete slipway
Suits:	all craft
Availability:	approx. 1½ hours either side HW
Restrictions:	use of site by prior arrangement only
Facilities:	fuel, parking for car and trailer (c), chandlery
Dues:	none
Charge:	min charge approx. £47
Directions:	from Conwy follow A55 expressway, turning onto A4087 to Bangor town centre and follow signs to Garth
Waters accessed:	Menai Straits, Conwy Bay and Irish Sea

Menai Bridge, Anglesey - Seafront

Type:	broad concrete slipway
Suits:	all craft
Availability:	all states of tide
Restrictions:	tides run very fast here and local advice should be taken before launching
Facilities:	fuel nearby, limited parking for car and trailer
Dues:	none
Charge:	none
Directions:	from Conwy follow A55/A5 over bridge turning into Beach Rd then Water Rd
Waters accessed:	Menai Straits, Conwy Bay and Irish Sea

Beaumaris, Anglesey - Anglesey Boat Co Ltd, Gallows Point
Tel: (0248) 810359

Type:	concrete slipway
Suits:	all craft
Availability:	approx. 3 hours either side HW 0900-1800 daily
Restrictions:	8 knot speed limit in main channel
Facilities:	fuel, parking for car and trailer, toilets, chandlery, outboard repairs and storage all on site: tractor and boat hoist also available
Dues:	none
Charge:	approx. £2.00
Directions:	from Menai Bridge follow A545 north east
Waters accessed:	Menai Straits, Conwy Bay and Irish Sea

Benllech, Anglesey - Seafront

Type:	concrete slipway onto sandy beach
Suits:	small craft which can be manhandled
Availability:	all states of tide
Restrictions:	8 knot speed limit: water-skiing permitted outside restricted area; site is suitable in settled conditions only
Facilities:	fuel nearby, parking for car and trailer
Dues:	none
Charge:	none
Directions:	from Menai Bridge follow A5025 for approx. 10 miles north then signs to Benllech Sands
Waters accessed:	Irish Sea

Amlwch, Anglesey - Marine Terminal
Tel: (0407) 831065 (Dockmaster)

Type:	steep concrete slipway in Inner Harbour
Suits:	all craft
Availability:	approx. 2 hours either side HW
Restrictions:	dead slow speed limit in harbour: this is a busy fishing and commercial harbour; narrow access to slipway
Facilities:	fuel nearby, parking for car and trailer on site, other facilities nearby
Dues:	none
Charge:	none
Directions:	from Menai Bridge follow A5025 north
Waters accessed:	Irish Sea

Cemaes Bay, Anglesey - Harbour Slipway

Type:	wide concrete slipway into small drying harbour
Suits:	all craft
Availability:	approx. 2 hours either side HW
Restrictions:	8 knot speed limit inshore: access can be very congested
Facilities:	fuel, parking for car and trailer
Dues:	none
Charge:	none
Directions:	from Menai Bridge follow A5025 north; site is on north coast of Anglesey
Waters accessed:	Irish Sea

Holyhead, Anglesey - Newry Beach
Tel: (0407) 762304 (Harbour Master)

Type:	concrete slipway
Suits:	all craft
Availability:	approx. 3 hours either side HW
Restrictions:	speed limit in harbour: water-skiing permitted offshore
Facilities:	fuel, parking for car and trailer, chandlery nearby
Dues:	none
Charge:	no
Directions:	from Menai Bridge follow A5 north to Holy Island: site is ¼ past Coastguard Station on right
Waters accessed:	Irish Sea

Llanfairpwll, Anglesey - Plas Coch Pub & Caravan Park
Tel: (0248) 714272/714295

Type:	concrete slipway
Suits:	small craft
Availability:	all states of tide
Restrictions:	use of site by prior arrangement only
Facilities:	no fuel, parking for car and trailer, toilets and showers
Dues:	none
Charge:	approx. £10
Directions:	from Conwy follow A55/A5 across Menai Bridge, turning left onto A4080
Waters accessed:	Menai Straits

Port Dinorwic - Port Dinorwic Yacht Harbour
Tel: (0248) 670559

Type:	concrete slipway
Suits:	all craft
Availability:	approx. 3-4 hours either side HW
Restrictions:	there are strong tidal currents here
Facilities:	diesel, parking for car and trailer (c), toilets, showers, crane, engine repairs, moorings
Dues:	approx. £7
Charge:	approx. £10
Directions:	from Bangor follow A487 west for approx. 3 miles turning off and following signs
Waters accessed:	Menai Strait

Plas Menai - Plas Menai National Watersports Centre
Tel: (0248) 670964

Type:	concrete slipway with winch
Suits:	small craft
Availability:	approx. 4 hours either side HW
Restrictions:	no speed limit; water-skiing permitted; prior notice is necessary and times are restricted by Centre use; launching is at owner's risk
Facilities:	fuel from garage, parking for car and trailer (c), toilets
Dues:	none known
Charge:	approx. £21.00
Directions:	from Bangor follow A487 west for approx. 4 miles; turn off and follow signs
Waters accessed:	Menai Strait

Pontllyfni

Type:	concrete slipway onto shingle and sand
Suits:	craft up to 15' LOA
Availability:	all states of tide
Restrictions:	none
Facilities:	fuel, parking for car and trailer
Dues:	none
Charge:	none
Directions:	from Caernarfon follow A487/499 towards Pwllheli: site is adjacent West Point Beach Holiday Camp
Waters accessed:	Caernarfon Bay

Trevor - Harbour Slipway

Type: concrete slipway
Suits: small craft
Availability: approx. 3 hours either side HW
Restrictions: 8 knot speed limit inshore
Facilities: no fuel, parking for car and trailer
Dues: none
Charge: none
Directions: from Caernarfon follow A487/499 towards Pwllheli and turn off right to Trevor: site is on Lleyn Peninsular
Waters accessed: Caernarfon Bay

Nefyn - Beach

Type: launching over hard shingle beach
Suits: small craft
Availability: all states of tide except LWS
Restrictions: 8 knot speed limit inshore: water-skiing permitted in designated area offshore
Facilities: no fuel, parking for car and trailer but not on beach
Dues: none
Charge: none
Directions: from Caernarfon follow A487/499 towards Pwllheli, turning onto B4417 at Llanaelhaearn: site is on north shore of Lleyn Peninsula
Waters accessed: Caernarfon Bay

Morfa-Nefyn - Porth Dinllaen Beach

Type: launching over hard shingle beach into sheltered north - facing bay
Suits: small craft
Availability: all states of tide except LWS
Restrictions: 8 knot speed limit inshore: water-skiing permitted in designated area offshore
Facilities: no fuel, parking for car and trailer but not on beach
Dues: none
Charge: none
Directions: from Caernarfon follow A487/499 towards Pwllheli, turning onto B4417 at Llanaelhaearn: site is on north shore of Lleyn Peninsula
Waters accessed: Caernarfon Bay

Abersoch - Abersoch Boatyard, The Saltings
Tel: (0758) 712213

Type: launching by tractor over shingle and sand beach
Suits: all craft

Availability:	all states of tide in working hours by prior arrangement
Restrictions:	8 knot speed limit inshore; water-skiing permitted in designated area offshore with access lane
Facilities:	fuel, parking for car and trailer, toilets, chandlery nearby
Dues:	none
Charge:	yes
Directions:	from Porthmadog follow A497/A499 west
Waters accessed:	Cardigan Bay

Abersoch - Porth Fawr

Type:	concrete slipway
Suits:	small craft
Availability:	all states of tide
Restrictions:	8 knot speed limit inshore; water-skiing permitted offshore
Facilities:	fuel nearby, parking for car and trailer (c), toilets in car park, chandlery in village
Dues:	none
Charge:	yes
Directions:	from Porthmadog follow A497/A499 west
Waters accessed:	Cardigan Bay

Abersoch - Golf Road Beach Entrance

Type:	concrete slipway onto firm sand
Suits:	all craft up to 20' LOA
Availability:	all states of tide 0600-2200
Restrictions:	8 knot speed limit inshore; water-skiing permitted in designated area offshore with access lane
Facilities:	fuel nearby, parking for car and trailer, chandlery in village
Dues:	none
Charge:	yes, pay car park attendant
Directions:	from Porthmadog follow A497/A499 to Abersoch village turning into Golf Rd: access to site is through car park
Waters accessed:	Cardigan Bay

Abersoch - Min-y-Don Boatyard
Tel: (0758) 740648 (evenings)

Type:	concrete slipway
Suits:	all craft up to 20' LOA
Availability:	all states of tide
Restrictions:	8 knot speed limit inshore; water-skiing permitted in designated area offshore with access lane
Facilities:	fuel nearby, limited parking for car and trailer on site, toilets nearby, other facilities in village
Dues:	none

Charge: approx. £10
Directions: from Porthmadog follow A497/A499 west to Abersoch: site is at bottom of hill and adjacent to the Lifeboat Station
Waters accessed: Cardigan Bay and Irish Sea

Pwllheli - Outer Harbour
Tel: (0758) 613131 ext.281 (Harbour Master)

Type: concrete slipway
Suits: all craft up to 20' LOA
Availability: approx. 3 hours either side HW
Restrictions: 6 knot speed limit in harbour; water-skiing permitted outside harbour
Facilities: fuel nearby, parking for car and trailer (c), toilets, chandlery and other boatyard facilities adjacent
Dues: none under 16' LOA: if over 16' LOA approx. £3.00
Charge: approx. £10
Directions: from Porthmadog follow A497 west: site is adjacent to Firmhelm Ltd
Waters accessed: Cardigan Bay and Irish Sea

Pwllheli - Outer Harbour (Wm Partington Marine Ltd)
Tel: (0758) 612808

Type: concrete slipway
Suits: all craft: winch available for larger craft
Availability: all states of tide, ask at chandlery shop
Restrictions: 5 mph speed limit in harbour: water-skiing permitted outside harbour
Facilities: fuel nearby, parking for car and trailer, chandlery, storage and repairs on site
Dues: none under 16' LOA; if over 16' LOA approx. £3.00
Charge: approx. £3.00
Directions: from town centre follow signs to Gimlet Rock Caravan Site
Waters accessed: North Cardigan Bay and Irish Sea

Pwllheli - Promenade

Type: concrete ramps onto sandy beach
Suits: small craft which can be manhandled
Availability: all states of tide
Restrictions: 8 knot speed limit inshore
Facilities: fuel nearby, parking for car and trailer, toilets and chandlers nearby
Dues: none
Charge: none
Directions: from Porthmadog follow A497 west
Waters accessed: North Cardigan Bay and Irish Sea

Porthmadog - Black Rock Sands

Type:	launching over firm beach
Suits:	small craft
Availability:	all states of tide
Restrictions:	8 knot speed limit inshore
Facilities:	no fuel, parking for car and trailer on beach
Dues:	none
Charge:	none
Directions:	from Porthmadog town centre follow road to Morfa Bychan and signs to beach
Waters accessed:	Tremadog Bay and Cardigan Bay

Porthmadog - Harbour Slipway
Tel: (0766) 512927 (Harbour Office)

Type:	concrete slipway
Suits:	all craft up to 23' LOA
Availability:	approx. 3 hours either side HW
Restrictions:	6 knot speed limit within harbour limit and 8 knots within designated safe bathing areas: water-skiing permitted outside these limits
Facilities:	fuel nearby, parking for car and trailer nearby, other facilities nearby
Dues:	none
Charge:	approx. £3.20
Directions:	from Conwy follow A470 turning onto A487: after crossing Britannia Bridge at N end of toll road, take first left: turn left again at 'T' junction into Lombard St and site is straight ahead
Waters accessed:	Tremadog Bay, North Cardigan Bay and Irish Sea

Porthmadog - The Tilewharf, Porthmadog & Trawsfynydd Sailing Club

Type:	steep concrete slipway with electric winch available
Suits:	dinghies only up to 17' LOA (no catamarans)
Availability:	approx. 3 hours either side HW
Restrictions:	6 knot speed limit within harbour limit and 8 knots within designated safe bathing areas: water-skiing permitted outside these limits: temporary membership of club needed
Facilities:	fuel, parking for car and trailer, crane by arrangement, toilets on site, chandlery nearby
Dues:	none
Charge:	yes
Directions:	from Conwy follow A470 turning onto A487: at Pen-y-Cei on west side of harbour follow narrow road right to end
Waters accessed:	Tremadog Bay, North Cardigan Bay and Irish Sea

Llanbedr, Shell Island
Tel: (0341) 23453

Type:	concrete slipway
Suits:	small craft only
Availability:	approx. 2½ hours either side HW
Restrictions:	obtain permission to launch from owners on site
Facilities:	no fuel, parking for car and trailer (c), toilets and other facilities on camp site: daily visitors welcome
Dues:	none
Charge:	approx. £2.00
Directions:	from Harlech follow A496 south; turn onto minor road by church in Llanbedr and follow for approx. 2 miles west: site is across causeway (impassable within 1 hour HW) on privately owned island
Waters accessed:	Tremadog Bay, Cardigan Bay and Irish Sea

Barmouth - Harbour Slipway
Tel: (0341) 280671 (Harbour Master)

Type:	concrete slipway onto soft sand
Suits:	all craft
Availability:	approx. 2½ hours either side HW by prior arrangement with Harbour Master
Restrictions:	5 knot speed limit: no jet skis; water-skiing permitted by licence (£9 per day)
Facilities:	diesel on site, petrol nearby, parking for car nearby (c), trailers may be left on site, toilets, chandlery and repairs available on site
Dues:	approx. £8.00
Charge:	no additional fee
Directions:	from Conwy follow A470 to Llaneltyd, turning onto A496: at Barmouth turn left under railway bridge; site is at mouth of estuary
Waters accessed:	Mawddach Estuary, Cardigan Bay and Irish Sea

Aberdovey - Dovey Inn Slipway
Tel: (0654) 767626 (Harbour Master)

Type:	concrete slipway onto hard-packed shingle and mud
Suits:	all craft
Availability:	all states of tide except 1 hour either side LWS
Restrictions:	5 knot speed limit within moorings: site can be congested; certificate of 3rd party insurance required
Facilities:	fuel (½ mile), parking for car (c), trailers may be left on beach, toilets nearby, crane by arrangement, chandlery and other facilities nearby
Dues:	yes
Charge:	yes
Directions:	from Cardigan follow A487 north, turn left onto A493 after Machynlleth
Waters accessed:	Dovey Estuary, Cardigan Bay and Irish Sea

Aberdovey - Dovey Yacht Club

Type:	concrete slipway onto sand
Suits:	dinghies only
Availability:	all states of tide
Restrictions:	5 knot speed limit within moorings: no powercraft allowed: temporary membership of club required - contact Secretary
Facilities:	fuel and parking for car and trailer (¼ mile) (c), crane , toilets on site; chandlery and repairs nearby
Dues:	none known
Charge:	yes
Directions:	turn off A487 north of Machynlleth onto A493 to Aberdovey
Waters accessed:	Dovey Estuary, Cardigan Bay and Irish Sea

Borth - Aber Leri Boatyard, Ynyslas
Tel: (0970) 871713

Type:	concrete slipway
Suits:	all craft
Availability:	approx. 2½ hours either side HW 0800-2100
Restrictions:	4 knot speed limit in moorings: jet skis prohibited
Facilities:	diesel nearby, parking for car and trailer (c) on site, toilets, chandlery, repairs and all yard services available on site
Dues:	none
Charge:	approx. £6.00
Directions:	follow B4572 north through Borth village for 1½ miles past golf course: site is adjacent river before bridge
Waters accessed:	River Leri, River Dovey, Cardigan Bay and Irish Sea

Borth - Beach Slipway
Tel: (0970) 611433 (Harbour Master)

Type:	concrete slipway
Suits:	all craft
Availability:	approx. 2 hours either side HW by prior arrangement with Harbour Master
Restrictions:	8 knot speed limit inshore: jet skis prohibited
Facilities:	fuel nearby, parking for car and trailer (c) nearby, toilets on site
Dues:	none
Charge:	none known
Directions:	from Aberystwyth follow A487 north, turning left onto B4572 to Borth
Waters accessed:	Cardigan Bay and Irish Sea

Aberystwyth - Harbour Slipway
Tel: (0970) 611433 (Harbour Master)

Type:	two concrete slipways
Suits:	all craft up to 20' LOA
Availability:	approx. 2 hours either side HW by prior arrangement with Harbour Master
Restrictions:	5 knot speed limit within harbour limits: water-skiing permitted outside these limits but jet skis are prohibited
Facilities:	fuel nearby, parking for car and trailer on site (c), toilets on site, chandlers nearby
Dues:	none
Charge:	approx. £3.50
Directions:	from Cardigan follow A487 north to town centre and then signs to harbour
Waters accessed:	Cardigan Bay and Irish Sea

Aberaeron - South Beach

Type:	concrete slipway
Suits:	all craft
Availability:	approx. 2½ hours either side HW for larger boats or at all states of tide for dinghies
Restrictions:	8 knots speed limit
Facilities:	fuel nearby, parking for car and trailer (c), toilets, showers
Dues:	none known
Charge:	yes
Directions:	from Cardigan follow A487 north
Waters accessed:	Cardigan Bay and Irish Sea

New Quay - Harbour Slipway
Tel: (0545) 560368 (Harbour Master)

Type:	concrete slipway
Suits:	all craft
Availability:	approx. 2 hours either side HW
Restrictions:	5 knot speed limit in harbour, 3 knot speed limit inshore: access to site is via steep one-way street
Facilities:	diesel on site, limited parking for car nearby and for trailer on site, toilets and nearby
Dues:	approx. £2.50
Charge:	approx. £2.50
Directions:	from Cardigan follow A487 north taking A486 west at Synod Inn
Waters accessed:	Cardigan Bay and Irish Sea

Llangranog - Slipway

Type: concrete slipway
Suits: dinghies and trailer-sailers
Availability: approx. 3 hours either side HW
Restrictions: 8 knot speed limit inshore: access to site is via narrow roads
Facilities: petrol, parking for car and trailer (c)
Dues: none
Charge: none
Directions: from Cardigan follow A487 north to Brynhoffnant, turn left onto B4334
Waters accessed: Cardigan Bay and Irish Sea

Traethsaith - Beach

Type: launching over shingle beach
Suits: small craft
Availability: all states of tide
Restrictions: 8 knot speed limit inshore: access to site is via narrow road
Facilities: no fuel, parking for car and trailer (c), toilets
Dues: none
Charge: none
Directions: follow A487 north from Cardigan, turning off onto minor roads at Tan-y-groes
Waters accessed: Cardigan Bay and Irish Sea

Aberporth - Slipway

Type: steep concrete slipway
Suits: dinghies and trailer-sailers
Availability: approx. 3 hours either side HW
Restrictions: 8 knot speed limit inshore: access to site is via narrow road
Facilities: petrol, parking for car and trailer (c), toilets
Dues: none
Charge: none
Directions: from Cardigan follow A487 north to Blaenannerch, turn left onto B4333
Waters accessed: Cardigan Bay and Irish Sea

Cardigan - St Dogmaels

Type: concrete slipway
Suits: craft up to 25' LOA
Availability: approx. 2 hours either side HW
Restrictions: speed limit in certain areas: beware strong currents
Facilities: no fuel, parking for car and trailer, toilets and pub nearby
Dues: none
Charge: none

Directions: from Cardigan follow B4546 through St Dogmaels: site is on west
bank of Teifi Estuary
Waters accessed: Teifi Estuary, Cardigan Bay and Irish Sea

Newport - Newport Sands
Tel: (0239) 820866

Type:	launching over hard sandy beach
Suits:	small craft which can be manhandled and sailboards
Availability:	all states of tide
Restrictions:	8 knot speed limit in estuary: sailboards must keep clear of bathing areas
Facilities:	parking for car and trailer on site (c), toilets, Inshore Rescue Boat
Dues:	none
Charge:	none
Directions:	from Newport take the coast road towards Moylgrove, turning left to beach after 2 miles
Waters accessed:	Newport Bay and Irish Sea

Newport - Parrog

Type:	concrete slipway onto hard sand
Suits:	craft up to 20' LOA and sailboards
Availability:	approx. 1½ hours either side HW
Restrictions:	8 knot speed limit in estuary: sailboards must keep clear of bathing areas: access road is narrow
Facilities:	fuel nearby, parking for car and trailer and toilets on site, chandlery and repairs nearby
Dues:	none
Charge:	none
Directions:	from Fishguard follow A487 to Newport: take minor road N following signs to 'Parrog' for ½ mile: access to site is through car park
Waters accessed:	Newport Bay and Irish Sea

Dinas Head - Cwym Yr Eglwys

Type:	concrete slipway onto sandy beach
Suits:	small craft which can be manhandled
Availability:	approx. 3 hours either side HW
Restrictions:	8 knot speed limit in bay: jet skis and water-skiing prohibited; site has narrow access road with sharp bend and is very congested in summer; beware strong currents off Dinas Head
Facilities:	limited parking for car (c) but little space for trailers
Dues:	none
Charge:	none
Directions:	from Fishguard follow A487 north turn left onto minor road after Dinas Cross for 1 mile: site is on east side of Dinas Head

Waters accessed: Newport Bay and Irish Sea

Dinas Head - Pwllgwaelod

Type:	concrete slipway onto hard sand
Suits:	small craft, sailboards and canoes
Availability:	all states of tide
Restrictions:	8 knots speed limit within 100m of shore: beware strong currents off Dinas Head
Facilities:	parking for car and trailer on site, toilets, pub and restaurant
Dues:	none
Charge:	none
Directions:	from Fishguard follow A487 north turning left onto minor road at Dinas Cross for 1 mile: site is on west side of Dinas Head

Waters accessed: Fishguard Bay and Irish Sea

Fishguard - Lower Town
Tel: (0348) 873231 (Harbour Master)

Type:	concrete slipway onto hard sand
Suits:	small craft, sailboards and canoes
Availability:	all states of tide
Restrictions:	6 knots speed limit in harbour: no water-skiing; access to site is very narrow and larger craft should use Goodwick slipway
Facilities:	no fuel, parking for car and trailer, toilets
Dues:	none
Charge:	none
Directions:	from Cardigan follow A487 south: site is at the end of the Quay

Waters accessed: Fishguard Bay and Irish Sea

Fishguard - Goodwick Slipway (Ferry Port)
Tel: (0348) 872881 (Harbour Master)

Type:	concrete slipway
Suits:	all craft
Availability:	approx. 2 hours either side HW
Restrictions:	speed limit in harbour: no water-skiing
Facilities:	fuel, parking for car and trailer, toilets, chandlery
Dues:	none known
Charge:	none
Directions:	from Cardigan follow A487 south: site is adjacent to car park on seafront

Waters accessed: Fishguard Bay and Irish Sea

Porthgain

Type:	steep concrete slipway onto rocky shore
Suits:	powered craft up to 20' LOA
Availability:	approx. 2 hours either side HW
Restrictions:	strong tide races just outside harbour make site unsuitable for dinghy sailing and water-skiing
Facilities:	fuel nearby, parking for car and trailer, toilets, pub and cafe on site
Dues:	none
Charge:	ask at pub
Directions:	from Fishguard follow A487 south to Croesgoch: turn right onto minor road to Porthgain for 2 miles

Waters accessed: Irish Sea

Abereiddy - Beach

Type:	steep concrete slipway onto soft sand
Suits:	sailing dinghies, sailboards and canoes
Availability:	approx. 4 hours either side HW
Restrictions:	8 knot speed limit within 100m of shore: trailers can get bogged down on beach; there are rocky patches and strong currents off-shore and large breakers build up on beach, especially in onshore winds
Facilities:	fuel nearby, parking for car and trailer on site, toilets
Dues:	none
Charge:	none
Directions:	from Fishguard follow A487 south through Croesgoch: turn right onto minor road signposted Abereiddy for 2 miles

Waters accessed: Irish Sea

St Davids Head - Porthclais

Type:	concrete slipway
Suits:	craft up to 25' LOA
Availability:	approx. 2½ hours either side HW
Restrictions:	speed limit inshore: slipway may be obstructed by locked barrier out of season
Facilities:	fuel from garage (2 miles), parking for car nearby, and for trailer on site, toilets, other facilities in St Davids (1½ miles)
Dues:	none
Charge:	none
Directions:	from Fishguard follow A487 south to St Davids then signs for Porthclais

Waters accessed: St Brides Bay and Irish Sea

Solva

Type:	concrete slipway
Suits:	small craft only
Availability:	approx. 2-3 hours either side HW
Restrictions:	8 knot speed limit: no water-skiing: a very beautiful site which is often congested in summer
Facilities:	fuel in village, parking for car and trailer, toilets
Dues:	none
Charge:	yes
Directions:	from St Davids follow A487 east: site is on north shore of bay and access is through car park
Waters accessed:	St Brides Bay and Irish Sea

Nolton Haven

Type:	launching across shingle and sand beach
Suits:	small craft only
Availability:	approx. 3 hours either side HW
Restrictions:	8 knot speed limit inshore: site is exposed in westerlys and bathing is dangerous at LW
Facilities:	petrol nearby, parking for car on site and for trailer nearby, toilets, pub, restaurant
Dues:	none
Charge:	none
Directions:	from Haverfordwest follow A487 west: turn left following signs to Nolton Haven 1 mile after Simpsons Cross
Waters accessed:	St Brides Bay and Irish Sea

Broad Haven

Type:	small concrete slipway onto hard sand
Suits:	small craft only
Availability:	all states of tide
Restrictions:	8 knot speed limit inshore: vehicles are allowed on beach to assist in launch and recovery; dangerous surf in W winds
Facilities:	fuel nearby, parking for car nearby and for trailer in designated park nearby (c), toilets nearby
Dues:	none
Charge:	none
Directions:	from Haverfordwest follow B4341 west
Waters accessed:	St Brides Bay and Irish Sea

Little Haven

Type: small concrete slipway onto beach
Suits: small craft
Availability: all states of tide
Restrictions: 8 knot speed limit inshore: no vehicles allowed on beach; access roads to site are steep
Facilities: fuel nearby, parking for car nearby (c),leave trailers to right of slipway or against left cliffside at LW, toilets
Dues: none
Charge: approx. £5.00 pa payable to Beach Officer
Directions: from Haverfordwest follow B4327 west to Hasguard Cross and then signs to Little Haven
Waters accessed: St Brides Bay and Irish Sea

Note: Slipway must be kept clear at all times for use of Lifeboat

Marloes - Martin's Haven

Type: concrete slipway onto steep pebble beach
Suits: small craft
Availability: approx. 2 hours either side HW
Restrictions: 8 knot speed limit inshore: site is within Skomer Marine Reserve Area where there are voluntary restrictions for craft; there are dangerous currents in Broad Sound
Facilities: fuel nearby, limited parking for car and trailer nearby (c), toilets
Dues: none
Charge: none
Directions: from Haverfordwest follow B4327 west towards Dale turning north onto minor road to Marloes
Waters accessed: St Brides Bay and Irish Sea

Dale - Dale Slipway
Tel: (0437) 764591 (Water Ranger)

Type: concrete slipway
Suits: craft up to 18-20' LOA
Availability: approx. 4-5 hours either side HW
Restrictions: 6 knot speed limit within 150m LW mark Apr-Sept: water-skiing permitted in designated area; narrow access road and site can be congested in summer
Facilities: fuel, parking for car and trailer nearby (c), toilets, other facilities from Dale Sailing Co nearby
Dues: none
Charge: none
Directions: from Haverfordwest follow B4327 west or minor roads from Milford Haven
Waters accessed: Milford Haven and Irish Sea

Gellyswick Bay
Tel: (0437) 764591 (Water Ranger)

Type:	wide concrete slipway onto hard sand
Suits:	all craft up to 40' LOA and 8' draught
Availability:	all states of tide except LWS
Restrictions:	slow speed in bay: water-skiing permitted in designated area; access is via a steep hill
Facilities:	fuel (1 mile), parking for car and trailer on site, toilets, other facilities from boatyards and marinas nearby
Dues:	none
Charge:	none
Directions:	from Milford Haven, take road past Hakin to Hubberston, turning left opposite petrol station and following road to Gellyswick Bay: site is opposite Pembrokeshire YC clubhouse
Waters accessed:	Milford Haven and Irish Sea

Neyland
Tel: (0437) 764591 (Water Ranger)

Type:	concrete slipway
Suits:	all craft up to 18'-20' LOA
Availability:	all states of tide except LWS
Restrictions:	water-skiing permitted in designated areas: beware strong tidal currents and eddies
Facilities:	fuel nearby, parking for car and trailer on site, other facilities nearby
Dues:	none
Charge:	none
Directions:	from Haverfordwest follow A4076 then A477: site is on Promenade next to Neyland YC
Waters accessed:	Milford Haven and Irish Sea

Burton
Tel: (0437) 764591 (Water Ranger)

Type:	concrete slipway onto rough stones and mud at LW
Suits:	small craft
Availability:	approx. 3 hours either side HW
Restrictions:	water-skiing permitted in designated areas: tidal currents can be strong here
Facilities:	fuel and other facilities from Neyland or Pembroke Dock, limited parking for car and trailer nearby
Dues:	none
Charge:	none
Directions:	from Haverfordwest follow A4076 then A477 to Cleddau Bridge, turning onto minor road to Burton
Waters accessed:	Cleddau River, Milford Haven and Irish Sea

Llangwm - Black Tar Point
Tel: (0437) 764591 (Water Ranger)

Type:	concrete slipway
Suits:	all craft up to approx. 18' LOA
Availability:	approx. 3 hours either side HW
Restrictions:	slow speed in mooring area: water-skiing permitted in designated areas; access road is narrow in places
Facilities:	fuel from garages nearby, limited parking for car and trailer, toilets nearby, other facilities from Neyland or Pembroke Dock
Dues:	none
Charge:	none, but donations to local Boating Assoc. appreciated
Directions:	from Haverfordwest follow A4076 south turning left onto minor roads and following signs to Black Tar Point: site is about 5 miles south of Haverfordwest

Waters accessed: Cleddau River, Milford Haven and Irish Sea

Haverfordwest - Old Quay, Quay Street
Tel: (0437) 764591 (Water Ranger)

Type:	very small concrete slipway
Suits:	small powered craft and canoes only
Availability:	approx. 2 hours either side HW
Restrictions:	low speed: access to site is narrow and bridge down river prohibits craft with masts from launching
Facilities:	fuel in town, parking for car in nearby car parks (c), other facilities from Neyland and Pembroke Dock
Dues:	none
Charge:	none
Directions:	from Carmarthen follow A40 west

Waters accessed: W. Cleddau River and Milford Haven

Landshipping Ferry - Foreshore
Tel: (0437) 764591 (Water Ranger)

Type:	launching over hard foreshore
Suits:	sailing dinghies, small powered craft and canoes
Availability:	all states of tide except LWS
Restrictions:	speed limit; site is in heart of National Park
Facilities:	no fuel, very limited parking for car and trailer on site
Dues:	none
Charge:	none
Directions:	from Carmarthen follow A40 west to Canaston Bridge, turning left onto A4075 to Cross Hands; turn right onto minor roads to Landshipping

Waters accessed: Cleddau River, Milford Haven and Irish Sea

Lawrenny - Lawrenny Yacht Station
Tel: (0646) 651212

Type:	concrete slipway
Suits:	all craft
Availability:	all states of tide
Restrictions:	4 knot speed limit in moorings
Facilities:	fuel, parking for car and trailer (c), toilets, showers, chandlery and other facilities
Dues:	none
Charge:	approx. £3.00
Directions:	from Carmarthen follow A40 and A477 west to Carew, turning right onto A4075 to Cresselly then following signposted minor roads
Waters accessed:	Cleddau River, Milford Haven and Irish Sea

Pembroke Dock - Pier Road, Hobbs Point
Tel: (0437) 764591 (Water Ranger)

Type:	broad, but steep, concrete slipway with drop at end at LW
Suits:	all craft
Availability:	approx. 4 hours either side HW
Restrictions:	speed limit: water-skiing and pwc permitted in designated areas nearby; beware strong currents and eddies: site is used by Pembroke Haven YC
Facilities:	fuel nearby, very limited parking for car and trailer on site, toilets on site, chandlery and repairs available nearby
Dues:	none
Charge:	none
Directions:	follow A477 into Pembroke Dock going down Pier Rd past Kwik Save supermarket to Hobbs Point
Waters accessed:	Milford Haven and Irish Sea

Pembroke Dock - Front Street
Tel: (0437) 764591 (Water Ranger)

Type:	concrete slipway which tends to silt up at bottom end
Suits:	small craft
Availability:	approx. 4 hours either side HW
Restrictions:	slow speed near slipway: water-skiing and pwc permitted in designated areas; site is used by Pembroke Haven Motor Boat Club
Facilities:	fuel, parking and other facilities available in Pembroke Dock
Dues:	none
Charge:	none
Directions:	follow A477 into Pembroke Dock, turning into Criterion Way and Front St.: site is at corner of Front St and Commercial Rd
Waters accessed:	Milford Haven and Irish Sea

Pembroke - Castle Pond

Tel: (0646) 622013 (Pembrokeshire Watersports School)

Type:	concrete slipway
Suits:	dinghies and canoes
Availability:	0900-1700 daily by arrangement with Pembrokeshire Watersports School
Restrictions:	access by prior arrangement only: on certain tides the pond is completely emptied
Facilities:	fuel nearby, limited parking for car and trailer on site (c), toilets on site, cafe and shops nearby
Dues:	none
Charge:	none
Directions:	turn off A4139 near Waterman's Arms into small public car park adjacent to Pembroke Castle
Waters accessed:	Castle Pond is above the Pembroke Barrage: passage of boats into the Pembroke River is allowed approx. 1 hour either side HW

Angle - Angle Bay

Tel: (0437) 764591 (Water Ranger)

Type:	concrete slipway
Suits:	craft up to 21' LOA
Availability:	approx. 2½ hours either side HW
Restrictions:	water-skiing permitted in designated areas nearby: narrow access road to site; area is part of National Park
Facilities:	fuel nearby, parking for car and trailer nearby, other facilities available from Pembroke Dock
Dues:	none
Charge:	none
Directions:	from Pembroke follow B4320 to Angle; turn right in village following signs to RNLI Lifeboat
Waters accessed:	Milford Haven, St George's Channel and Irish Sea

Freshwater East

Type:	steep concrete slipway onto sandy beach which is soft in places
Suits:	small craft at all times; larger craft need 4-wheel drive vehicle to tow across beach
Availability:	all states of tide
Restrictions:	navigate with due care and attention: access road is narrow; no parking on beach
Facilities:	limited parking for car and trailer nearby (c), toilets
Dues:	none
Charge:	none
Directions:	from Pembroke follow A4139 east to Lamphey; turn right onto B4584 and follow signs
Waters accessed:	Carmarthen Bay

Lydstep Haven - Lydstep Beach Holiday Resort
Tel: (0834) 871871

Type:	steep concrete slipway onto hard sandy beach
Suits:	all craft except jet skis
Availability:	all states of tide 0900-1800
Restrictions:	speed limit; water-skiing permitted outside buoys off beach; pwc prohibited; proof of insurance required
Facilities:	no fuel, limited parking for car and trailer (c) and toilets on site
Dues:	none
Charge:	approx. £10.00
Directions:	from Tenby follow A4139 west towards Pembroke and follow signs to Lydstep Haven

Waters accessed: Carmarthen Bay

Tenby - Harbour Slipway
Tel: (0834) 842717 (Harbour Office, Castle Square)

Type:	concrete slipway onto hard sand
Suits:	craft up to 16' LOA
Availability:	approx. 2½ hours either side HW by arrangement
Restrictions:	3 knot speed limit in Inner Harbour, 10 knots in Outer Harbour: water-skiing permitted in designated area but pwc prohibited: site is very congested in summer and access is via very narrow and busy town centre roads with steep road into basin
Facilities:	fuel in town, very limited parking for car and trailer (c), toilets, cafes and restaurants on site, limited chandlery nearby
Dues:	approx. £1.80 (sailing craft) or £5.64 (other craft)
Charge:	approx. £1.79 (sailing craft) or £1.90 (other craft)
Directions:	from Carmarthen follow A40/A477/A478 to Tenby: turn off along Narberth Rd to North Beach, going through Tudor Sq. (town centre) to harbour: site is adjacent to Tenby SC

Waters accessed: Carmarthen Bay

Saundersfoot - Harbour Slipway
Tel: (0834) 812094 (Harbour Office)

Type:	concrete slipway onto hard sand
Suits:	all craft
Availability:	approx. 2½ hours either side HW or at all states of tide for dinghies
Restrictions:	3 knot speed limit in harbour, 5 knots within 250yds of shore: water-skiing permitted in designated area: certificate of insurance cover required: site can be congested in summer
Facilities:	fuel (1 mile), parking for car and trailer (c), toilets, chandlery nearby
Dues:	approx. £3.90 incl. parking for car and trailer
Charge:	no additional charge
Directions:	from Carmarthen follow A40/A477/A478 to Pentlepoir: turn left

onto B4316 to Saundersfoot
Waters accessed: Carmarthen Bay

Amroth - Amroth Beach

Type:	steep L-shaped concrete slipway
Suits:	craft up to approx.16' LOA
Availability:	approx. 1 hour either side HW or across beach at other times
Restrictions:	all vessels to operate 500 yds offshore: no vehicles or trailers to remain on beach
Facilities:	no fuel, parking for car and trailer nearby, toilets nearby
Dues:	none
Charge:	none
Directions:	from Carmarthen follow A40/A477 to Llanteg: turn left onto minor roads to Amroth village and follow road along coast to Amroth Castle: site is adjacent Amroth Castle Caravan Park

Waters accessed: Carmarthen Bay

Laugharne - Beach

Type:	launching over hard shingle beach
Suits:	small craft only
Availability:	approx. 2 hours either side HW
Restrictions:	none known
Facilities:	fuel in village, parking for car and trailer, toilets
Dues:	none
Charge:	none
Directions:	from Carmarthen follow A40 to St Clears turning left onto A4066: site is by Castle

Waters accessed: Taf Estuary and Carmarthen Bay

Llangain - Towy Boat Club, Llanstephan Road

Type:	launching over shingle
Suits:	small craft only
Availability:	approx. 2 hours either side HW
Restrictions:	5 knot speed limit
Facilities:	no fuel, parking for car and trailer
Dues:	none
Charge:	yes
Directions:	from Carmarthen follow B4312 south

Waters accessed: River Towy and Carmarthen Bay

Carmarthen - The Quay (Carmarthen Boat Club)

Type:	steep concrete slipway
Suits:	small powercraft only
Availability:	approx. 2 hours either side HW
Restrictions:	5 knot speed limit: water-skiing permitted in designated area; headroom restricted downriver
Facilities:	fuel from garage nearby, parking for car and trailer (c)
Dues:	none
Charge:	yes
Directions:	site is off A40
Waters accessed:	River Towy and Carmarthen Bay

Ferryside - River Towy Yacht Club

Type:	concrete slipway
Suits:	all craft
Availability:	approx. 2 hours either side HW with permission
Restrictions:	5 knot speed limit in moorings: water-skiing permitted in designated area; best site in area
Facilities:	fuel by arrangement, parking for car and trailer (c), toilets
Dues:	none
Charge:	yes
Directions:	from Carmarthen follow A48/A484 south: turn off at LLandyfaelog and follow signs
Waters accessed:	River Towy and Carmarthen Bay

Kidwelly - Quay

Type:	concrete slipway
Suits:	all craft
Availability:	approx. 2 hours either side HW
Restrictions:	none known
Facilities:	fuel in village, parking for car and trailer
Dues:	none
Charge:	none
Directions:	from Carmarthen follow A48/A484 south: site is 1 mile SW of Kidwelly and access is via Station Rd and over railway line
Waters accessed:	River Gwendraeth and Carmarthen Bay

Burry Port - Harbour Slipway
Tel: (0554) 834315 (Harbour Master)

Type:	four concrete slipways
Suits:	all craft
Availability:	approx. 3 hours either side HW

Restrictions:	3 knot speed limit within harbour limits: water-skiing permitted in Burry Inlet: the bar at the entrance is dangerous in strong W winds
Facilities:	fuel nearby, parking for car and trailer on site, toilets, chandlery and repairs all available on site
Dues:	none
Charge:	none
Directions:	turn off M4 at junction 48, taking the A4138 to Llanelli and then A484 to Burry Port
Waters accessed:	Burry Inlet, River Loughor and Carmarthen Bay

Llanelli - Lledi Basin Slipway

Type:	concrete slipway
Suits:	all craft
Availability:	all states of tide
Restrictions:	speed limit: water-skiing permitted in Burry Inlet
Facilities:	fuel (¼ mile), parking for car and trailer
Dues:	none
Charge:	none
Directions:	turn off M4 at junction 48, taking the A4138 to Llanelli: site is ½ mile south of town centre and access is via Queen Victoria Rd and Cambrian St turning right along track across open ground
Waters accessed:	Burry Inlet, River Loughor and Carmarthen Bay

Mumbles - Knab Site, Southend

Type:	two concrete slipways
Suits:	all craft
Availability:	approx. 4-5 hours either side HW
Restrictions:	4 knot speed limit in moorings
Facilities:	fuel (1 mile), parking for car and trailer (c), toilets (200yds), chandlery in Swansea: temporary membership of club available
Dues:	none
Charge:	none
Directions:	from Swansea follow A4067 west to Mumbles: site is opposite Mumbles YC
Waters accessed:	Swansea Bay

Swansea - Swansea Yacht and Sub-Aqua Club, Pocketts Wharf
Tel: (0792) 654863

Type:	concrete slipway
Suits:	all craft except skiboats and pwc
Availability:	at all times by arrangement with Club Bosun or Secretary
Restrictions:	4 knot speed limit: water-skiing and pwc prohibited
Facilities:	fuel nearby, parking for car nearby and for trailer on site, toilets and showers in clubhouse, chandlery and repairs nearby

Dues:	none
Charge:	approx. £5.00
Directions:	leave M4 at junction 47 taking A483 to Swansea: site adjoins East Burrows Rd

Waters accessed: River Tawe and Swansea Bay (via lock)

Swansea - Swansea Marina, Lockside
Tel: (0792) 470310

Type:	launching by boat hoist only into locked marina basin
Suits:	trailer-sailers
Availability:	0800-1600 by prior arrangement
Restrictions:	4 knot speed limit: lock gates open for 3½ hours either side HW
Facilities:	diesel on site, parking for car and trailer (c), toilets, chandlery and repairs all available on site
Dues:	none
Charge:	approx. £40
Directions:	leave M4 at junction 47 and take A483 to Swansea: follow signs to Marina from City Centre

Waters accessed: Swansea Bay (via lock) and Bristol Channel

Neath - Monkstone Marina, (Monkstone Cruising and Sailing Club)
Tel: (0639) 641238 or (0792) 812229

Type:	concrete slipway
Suits:	small powered craft, sailing dinghies and trailer-sailers with up to 6' draught
Availability:	approx. 2 hours either side HW by prior arrangement
Restrictions:	4 knot speed limit on river: M4 construction work may temporarily affect access
Facilities:	diesel on site, petrol from garage (½ mile), parking for car and trailer, showers and toilets on site: other facilities from Swansea
Dues:	included in launching fee
Charge:	approx. £11.75
Directions:	leave M4 at junction 42, following A48 over River Neath and turning left onto A483 to Swansea South Docks; take 1st left to Monkstone Marina

Waters accessed: River Neath, Swansea Bay and Bristol Channel

Port Talbot - Aberavon Beach

Type:	two concrete slipways onto beach
Suits:	craft up to 20' LOA
Availability:	all states of tide
Restrictions:	speed limit inshore
Facilities:	fuel, parking for car and trailer, toilets
Dues:	none

Charge: none
Directions: leave M4 at junction 41 and follow signs
Waters accessed: Swansea Bay and Bristol Channel

Porthcawl - Harbour Slipway
Tel: (0656) 782756

Type: steep concrete slipway
Suits: small craft
Availability: approx. 3 hours either side HW 0900-2100
Restrictions: speed limit: access to slipway has low overhead telephone cables; priority must be given to RNLI Lifeboat
Facilities: fuel nearby, parking for car and trailer on site, toilets nearby
Dues: none
Charge: approx. £2.40
Directions: leave M4 at junction 37 taking A4229 and following signs to seafront
Waters accessed: Bristol Channel

Barry - Sully Slipway, Hayes Road
Tel: (0446) 709563

Type: concrete slipway
Suits: all craft
Availability: approx. 3 hours either side HW
Restrictions: none
Facilities: fuel nearby, parking for car and trailer on site
Dues: none
Charge: none
Directions: leave M4 at junction 33 taking A4232 /A4050 south to Barry following signs to Barry Dock: at roundabout at link road take turning for Sully and 2nd left at next roundabout: site is behind civic amenity site
Waters accessed: Severn Estuary and Bristol Channel

Barry - Watch Tower Bay, The Knap
Tel: (0446) 709563

Type: concrete slipway
Suits: small craft
Availability: approx. 3 hours either side HW
Restrictions: speed limit: pwc prohibited: vehicles prohibited from slipway
Facilities: parking for car nearby, limited space for trailers on site, toilets nearby
Dues: none
Charge: annual permit required (£5, numbers limited)
Directions: leave M4 at junction 33 and take A4232 /A4050 south to Barry following signs to 'The Knap'

Waters accessed: Severn Estuary and Bristol Channel

Penarth - Northern Slipway, The Esplanade
Tel: (0446) 709565

Type:	narrow and steep concrete slipway
Suits:	small craft
Availability:	approx. 3 hours either side HW
Restrictions:	8 knot speed limit inshore
Facilities:	fuel nearby, parking for car and trailer (c) and toilets on site
Dues:	none
Charge:	annual permit required (£5, numbers limited)
Directions:	leave M4 at junction 33 taking A4232 to Penarth and following signs through town to seafront: site is situated under the multi-storey car park

Waters accessed: Severn Estuary and Bristol Channel

Penarth - Southern Slipway
Tel: (0446) 709563

Type:	concrete slipway with sharp bend
Suits:	sailing craft and small powered craft (under 25hp)
Availability:	approx. 3 hours either side HW
Restrictions:	speed limit: powered craft over 25hp and jet skis prohibited
Facilities:	fuel nearby, parking for car and trailer nearby, toilets nearby
Dues:	none
Charge:	annual permit required (£5,numbers limited)
Directions:	leave M4 at junction 33 taking A4232 to Penarth and following signs through town to seafront: site is in front of YC

Waters accessed: Severn Estuary and Bristol Channel

Rudyard, Staffs - Rudyard Lake
Tel: (0538) 33280 (Information Centre)

Type:	concrete slipway
Suits:	sailing craft up to 28' LOA
Availability:	during daylight hours
Restrictions:	powered craft prohibited: narrow access road
Facilities:	parking for car and trailer (c) and toilets on site
Dues:	none
Charge:	approx. £4.50
Directions:	from Leek follow A523 north for 3 miles, turning left to Rudyard: at roundabout turn right and immediately right again into Lake Rd: entrance is 250yds on right

Waters accessed: Rudyard Lake only